# A CONCEPTUAL FRAMEWORK
## FOR
## MENTAL HEALTH RESEARCH
## ON
## HISPANIC POPULATIONS

# A CONCEPTUAL FRAMEWORK
# FOR
# MENTAL HEALTH RESEARCH
# ON
# HISPANIC POPULATIONS

*BY*
LLOYD H. ROGLER
*and*
ROSEMARY SANTANA COONEY
GIUSEPPE COSTANTINO
BRIAN F. EARLEY
BETH GROSSMAN
DOUGLAS T. GURAK
ROBERT MALGADY
ORLANDO RODRIGUEZ

*With the assistance of:*
KEVIN COLLERAN
PATRICIA ELWELL
EDNA SCHRODER GUERRERO
EMILY KLASS
YVONNE MARTINEZ WARD

MONOGRAPH NO. 10

Hispanic Research Center
Lloyd H. Rogler, *Director*

# HISPANIC RESEARCH CENTER
# FORDHAM UNIVERSITY
# BRONX, NEW YORK 10458

## MONOGRAPH SERIES

The Hispanic Research Center is supported by
Research Grant 2PO1 MH 30569-06A1 from the
National Institute of Mental Health,
Center for Minority Group Mental Health Programs.

# CONTENTS

# PREFACE

From its inception, one purpose of the Hispanic Research Center has been to present information on topical areas relevant to Hispanic concerns in an effort to raise critically important questions of research and policy. Thus, two issues of the Center's *Research Bulletin* (October 1981-January 1982; April-July 1982) presented a new conceptual framework to review and integrate the literature on epidemiological and clinical service research regarding the mental health of Hispanics. Many of the readers of the *Research Bulletin* found the information contained in those issues to be of value in charting important paths for research and public policy affecting Hispanics. Because of the interest that the subject has aroused in our readers, we take pleasure in presenting a revised version of the originally published articles entitled, "A New Conceptual Framework for Mental Health Clinical Service Research on Hispanic Populations," in this single volume. Several parts of the original articles have been rewritten for this edition to incorporate substantially new material and research developments.

The readers of our monograph series will note the heavy empirical emphasis in our previous monographs which have focused largely on presenting data and research findings. On this occasion, however, we see the need to take stock and theoretically order the work we and others have done thus far. The construction of a conceptual framework for mental health clinical research attempts to capture not only our own research but also that of others reflected in the literature on the subject. It also coincides with the recommendations made by the Special Populations Sub-Task Panel in the *Report to the President's Commission on Mental Health* (1978) calling for both applied and basic research of a programmatic nature. After examining a comprehensive bibliography on the mental health of Hispanics, the report states that this research literature has not yet attained the status of an integrated body of scientific knowledge. The conceptual framework we present here is intended to make a contribution to attaining that status.

Even though we have developed this five-stage framework in response to our own needs to conceptualize our work on Hispanic mental health issues and as a contribution to the recommendation made by the Special Populations Sub-Task Panel on Mental Health of Hispanic Americans, it is important to emphasize that the framework is not uniquely linked either to Hispanics or to issues of mental health. Its value transcends important issues

v

of Hispanic mental health. The framework delineates a hypothetical process that can be used to review and conceptualize the literature on populations other than Hispanics and in disease patterns other than mental illness. We strongly invite others to use the framework described in these pages in reference to other groups, both minority and non-minority, and in reference to non-mental health conditions.

The reader will note that a number of people contributed to the preparation of this volume. The senior author of this monograph, Lloyd H. Rogler, was responsible for organizing the conceptual framework and for the drafting of the overarching statement. Rosemary Santana Cooney and Douglas T. Gurak, both Senior Research Associates of the Hispanic Research Center, assisted with the theoretical formulation of the material concerning migration and mental health in the first phase of the framework. In addition, Dr. Cooney took part in analyzing the research related to acculturation and the intergenerational family process presented in the second phase; while Dr. Gurak contributed the findings of his study on the epidemiological processes associated with variations in anxiety status among Dominican and Colombian immigrants found in the first phase. The other co-authors of this volume are all Research Associates of the Hispanic Research Center. Giuseppe Costantino, author of the TEMAS projective personality test and of the folktale therapeutic modality for Hispanic children, prepared the material on those topics found in the third and fourth phases of the framework, respectively. He was assisted in this task by Robert Malgady who also drew up the section concerning the impact of bilingualism and biculturalism found in the third phase of the framework. Brian F. Earley assisted in reading and organizing the literature for the second phase of the framework. Beth Grossman assisted in reading and shaping the general literature review for the third, fourth, and fifth phases. Orlando Rodriguez participated in formulating the second phase of the model, particularly in presenting the research illustrating the components of this phase. Throughout these processes, a massive body of literature was examined and analyzed by Kevin Colleran, Patricia Elwell, Edna Schroder Guerrero, Emily Klass, and Yvonne Martinez Ward, all graduate students who worked as research assistants for this project. In addition, the Center's editor, Stasia Madrigal, edited successive drafts of the manuscript.

This monograph is the tenth in a series published by the Hispanic Research Center to stimulate interest in Hispanic concerns. The Hispanic Research Center was established at Fordham University in 1977, under a grant from the National Institute of Mental Health, renewed in 1982, to work toward five major objectives: (1) to develop and conduct policy-relevant epidemiological-clinical services research on processes relevant to Hispanic mental health; (2) to increase the small pool of scholars trained in Hispanic mental health research and to upgrade their research skills through the provision of apprenticeship training and other mechanisms; (3) to provide technical assistance to organizations and individuals interested in the mental health problems of Hispanic populations; (4) to provide a clearinghouse function for the publication and dissemination of mental health materials relevant to Hispanics; and (5) to develop a research environment for scholars from the mental health disciplines.

With the publication of this monograph we hope to highlight an area of Hispanic mental health research which in the past has been frequently characterized by shifting issues and theories. This research has tended to move from one topical area to another as if it had thoroughly posed and mastered the significant questions and provided reliable data. In this volume, we call attention to the fact that there are many basic problems to be resolved in the area of Hispanic mental health. Issues in this area are still in need of competent research attention, innovative formulations, and research-based recommendations relevant to mental health policy.

Lloyd H. Rogler
*Director, Hispanic Research Center*
*Fordham University*

*March 1983*

# A CONCEPTUAL FRAMEWORK
# FOR MENTAL HEALTH RESEARCH
# ON HISPANIC POPULATIONS

The purpose of this volume is to organize selected portions of the literature on Hispanic mental health according to a conceptual framework encompassing clinical service research. Although sparse in general, the literature on Hispanic mental health is more available for Puerto Ricans and Mexican Americans than it is for other Hispanic groups such as Cubans and Dominicans. Therefore, the review of the literature presented here focuses mainly on Puerto Ricans and Mexican Americans. Our review of this literature, however, is not comprehensive, since extensive reviews of the literature on this topic are elsewhere available to the interested reader.[1] The need for a comprehensive framework for mental health research, such as is found in these pages, is evident in the data presented by the *Report to the President's Commission on Mental Health* (1978). The report notes that there are over 2000 published works on the mental health of the Hispanic population, with over 75 percent published since 1970. However, the report laments the fact that "quality has not kept pace with quantity and the research literature on Hispanic mental health has yet to attain the status of an integrated body of scientific knowledge. It remains plagued by stereotypic interpretations, weak methodological and data-analytical techniques, lack of replicability of findings and the absence of programmatic research."[2] Because Hispanics represent the most rapidly growing minority group in the United States, there is a pressing need to improve the quality of such research. Already the second largest minority group, Hispanics may outnumber the black population in the next quarter century. This rapid growth must be viewed in the context of substantial diversity in national origin, demographic profile, migration status, and settlement patterns.[3] In sum, flawed research lacking integration has addressed the important issue of mental health among Hispanics, a rapidly growing and diverse population.

The presentation of a conceptual framework for clinical service research, we believe, will serve a variety of purposes, all having to do with

1

the widely recognized and above-noted need of integrating the literature. The framework will enable us to locate the goals and findings of specific research projects in a broader conceptual structure; to examine the inter-relationship of research findings; to identify important gaps in the research, unaddressed by the literature; and to examine and then formulate critically important problems located within the framework. We view our effort as tentative and exploratory, but characterized by innovativeness.

In broad terms, we conceptualize clinical service research as spanning a hypothetical temporal sequence. From the beginning to the end, the sequence is divided into five phases which sometimes overlap: the first phase involves the emergence of mental health problems; the second phase involves intricate help-seeking behaviors which may lead the person to contact official mental health service providers; the third phase involves attempts — valid or invalid — by such help providers to evaluate or diagnose the client's psychological condition; the fourth phase begins when official mental health providers attempt to deal with the problem through therapeutic interventions; and the fifth phase involves the termination of treatment and the client's attempted resumption of customary social roles, relieved of the original problem or not. Clinical service research is any research which focuses upon at least one of these five phases. The research can be descriptively oriented to profile aspects of the phases, or analytically oriented to explain dimensions of the phases. Included, too, are innovative efforts to create and test the efficacy of diagnostic procedures and treatment modalities.

The application of this framework to specific cases of persons experiencing psychological problems would undoubtedly show a variety of patterns or trajectories across the several phases: the duration of the entire sequence could be short or long; some persons experiencing psychological distress may never reach the official help providers, but remain in the population at large, identifiable only by means of true prevalence epidemiological research; others may move through several phases and, with the original problem resolved, resume their customary social roles; some persons may move through the different phases without relieving or eliminating the original problem which stimulated the help-seeking effort; some persons may not pass through all phases of the sequence; or some may move back and forth through a few of the phases. Clearly, there are many other possibilities. Thus, when projected against the framework, specific instances involving persons in any phase of the framework will show considerable variety. However, the application of the sequential framework enables research-relevant distinctions to be made in charting the history of attempts to cope with psychological problems.

The sequential framework invites the use of a temporal perspective in examining assumptions commonly held by mental health practitioners and researchers. For example, it is commonly believed that success in either phases three, four, or five presupposes success in the preceding phase(s). For

2

the psychological problem to be diagnosed correctly, the client must first come into contact with a help giver who can conduct the appropriate diagnostic procedure. Moreover, appropriate treatment presupposes a correct diagnosis. Finally, the client's successful resumption of customary social roles depends not only upon the efficacy of the treatment received, but also upon a combination of factors associated with the person's life circumstances. We present these assumptions in their simplest terms, realizing fully that the actual clinical service sequence is substantially more complicated. Nonetheless, we believe there is value in the use of such simplifications in providing an overview of the clinical service research literature focusing upon Hispanics. The literature indicates that Hispanics experience pronounced difficulties in each of the five phases: there is very little reliable epidemiological data on the prevalence and incidence of psychological distress in the Hispanic population; Hispanics underutilize mental health services in relation to their mental health needs; they are prone to be misdiagnosed because of culturally insensitive diagnostic procedures; the treatment they receive does not fit their culture and life circumstances; and, finally, they experience difficulty in resuming their customary social roles after undergoing treatment. The phases comprise successive barriers — as if they were an obstacle course — which keep Hispanics from moving effectively through the sequence.

# *Phase 1:*
# EMERGENCE OF
# MENTAL HEALTH PROBLEMS

The approaches to the study of the emergence of mental health problems in the Hispanic population can be as varied as the diverse methodologies used to study the etiologic factors of mental illness. We make the assumption, however, that when a population has hardly been studied and our information is sparse, and reliable knowledge is practically nonexistent, the type of study most likely to provide a basis for fruitful work in the future should be broadly delineated in its scope to cover diversity in sociocultural and economic factors. Thus, psychiatric epidemiology is the indicated method in the initiation of this phase of the framework.

Research in psychiatric epidemiology, seeking to determine the true prevalence and incidence rates of mental health problems, has a double relevance to our effort to understand Hispanic mental health. First, by identifying variations in the mental health status of persons across demographic categories and sociocultural groups, such research provides clues relevant to the etiology of mental distress. Thus, much of the rapidly increasing research on the interconnections between stress, changing life events, supportive networks, and mental health is rooted historically in the findings that disadvantaged, marginated groups experience disproportionate mental distress. (The concept of stress, in all of its rich sociopsychological meaning, is postulated to mediate between the overarching structure of society and the specific life circumstances of persons. Elsewhere[4] we have used this body of literature to develop a series of theoretical ideas linking the Hispanics' experience of migration-induced life stresses to psychological impairment and patterns of mental health utilization.) Such research is oriented toward uncovering factors relevant to the sociocultural and psychological origins of mental health distress. Second, psychiatric epidemiology provides empirically based measures of variations in the need for mental health care across demographic categories and sociocultural groups. Findings relevant to etiology and those describing rates of mental health problems, as we shall see, have been important in assaying the mental health needs of Hispanics.

Arguments for increased mental health care for Hispanics are based partly upon psychiatric epidemiology research indicating that populations with the demographic, socioeconomic, and experiential characteristics of Hispanics present comparatively higher rates of mental illness. Empirical relationships relevant to etiology — whether only hypothesized or confirmed by research — are generalized to subsume the situation of Hispanics. Thus the classic study by Hollingshead and Redlich,[5] confirming an inverse relationship between socioeconomic status and some forms of treated illness, is relevant to the situation of Hispanics: their low socioeconomic characteristics, particularly of subgroups such as Mexican Americans and Puerto Ricans, render them vulnerable to mental health problems. The confirmation of the Hollingshead and Redlich hypothesis, replicated in a variety of settings and in reference to the relationship between schizophrenia and socioeconomic factors,[6] strengthens the application of the inference to Hispanics.

Similarly, there is a long history of reserach on the relationship between migration and mental health, most of it based upon hospital admission or treatment records.[7] This research exhibits widely recognized methodological problems associated with the study of self-selected institutionalized populations: the inability to introduce appropriate controls in comparisons between migrants and non-migrants;[8] the operational specification of the concepts of migrant or migration;[9] the analysis of undifferentiated categories of "all mental disorders";[10] and the global categories (schizophrenia) subject to unknown margins of diagnostic error.[11] Whatever the methodological shortcomings of such research, there are in fact substantially good reasons for believing, along with Rendon,[12] that there is a relationship between migration and mental illness. Migration from one sociocultural system to another that is different creates new sources of continuing stress which impinge upon the emotional life of the migrant. However diverse their migratory experiences,[13] first-generation Hispanics are subjected to migration-induced stressful experiences.

The Canino, Earley, and Rogler study[14] of Puerto Rican children in New York City provides a specific example of how such evidence is used to affirm the need for increased mental health care for Puerto Ricans. The authors present various socioeconomic indicators, such as income, education, and unemployment, to show that Puerto Ricans on the mainland are a severely disadvantaged minority group. They are the least educated and least skilled subgroup in the general population; they are hindered by language difficulties; they have the highest unemployment rate, the lowest-paying jobs, the lowest income, and the highest percentage of families living at or below the poverty level. In addition to their low socioeconomic position, Puerto Ricans experience qualitatively new types of stress-inducing life events: the need to learn a new language; the impact of bilingualism upon information processing, memory, cognitive abilities, personality characteristics, and world views; prejudice and discrimination; adaptation to the impersonal terms of a bureaucratized society; the demands of an agitated daily cycle of life in an urban metropolis; and the tribulations and confusions of daily interactions with persons outside their ethnic group. The profile of Puerto Ricans developed by the authors coincides substantially with epidemiological models of a population with a high risk for mental illness. Thus, the Puerto Ricans' comparatively high mental health needs are established by inferences. Such inferences are not to be confused with speculation: they are an integral part of the deductive method in scientific predictions.

Nonetheless, there is a commonly recognized need for epidemiological studies to determine the mental health of Hispanics by measuring dimensions of mental health or by classifying respondents directly according to diagnostic categories of mental illness. Unfortunately, such studies are extremely rare. For example, in a recent systematic review of the literature, Roberts[15] ". . . identified only three papers, all quite modest in scope . . ." reporting population-based data of the incidence and prevalence of psychological disorder among Mexican Americans. The findings on the comparative distress of Mexican Americans and other groups were mixed. Roberts' own study in Alameda County, California, suggests that ". . . the prevalence of psychological distress among Chicanos is at least as high as in the overall population and, in some respects, higher."[16]

With respect to Puerto Ricans in New York City, an earlier major study of residents of midtown Manhattan conducted by Srole et al.[17] found that about half of the 27 Puerto Ricans in its sample were diagnosed as having severe or incapacitating symptoms. While the number of Puerto Ricans in the survey was quite small, this rate was double the rate for any other subgroup in the study. Later evaluation of this study suggested that the differential indications of mental illness may have been due to a bias in the research methodology and to cultural differences.[18] In a survey of more than 1000 residents in the Washington Heights section of New York City, Dohrenwend and Dohrenwend[19] found that Puerto Ricans reported significantly greater numbers of psychiatric symptoms than their social class counterparts in other ethnic groups. They noted that some of the observed differences may have been due to methodological factors such as cultural differences in response styles, language used to express psychological distress, and concepts of socially desirable behavior. The root issue is measurement error, or the way in which factors accompanying the measurement of mental illness, but conceptually extraneous to mental illness, intrude upon the observed assessment. Thus, variability in the extent to which respondents are acquiescent or overcompliant in answering questions pertaining to their mental health, or see items in a mental health instrument as representing variable degrees of social desirability, does affect the observed mental health assessments. One conclusion seems almost inevitable: in the absence of well-designed community-based epidemiological research which disentangles important sources of measurement error, the case for comparatively high

Whether established inferentially or empirically, the mental health status of Hispanic populations is a core element in the first phase of the clinical service framework presented here. It must be given careful attention in any attempt to understand the Hispanics' utilization of mental health services. At the same time, the rates of mental health symptoms or problems must be kept analytically separate from clinic admission rates, rates of specific types of treated mental disorders, or rates of utilization of mental health facilities. To confuse these statistics leads to errors in research and possible misjudgment in mental health policy. Statistics based upon the records of treatment facilities represent the outcome of complicated community-based social, psychological and cultural processes, and more than likely do not have a stable correlation with true prevalence rates across social and have a stable correlation with true prevalence rates across social and cultural groups in the population at large. Were treatment statistics to be taken as a proxy for true mental health rates — thus, disregarding the process separating the two — biases would intrude into the effort to understand Hispanic mental health service needs. Methodologically, by keeping both as separate components of the clinical service framework's first phase, we can clarify some of the confusion which underlies the literature regarding the hypothesis that Hispanics underutilize mental health facilities.[20] We do not dispute the hypothesis, but we do raise questions regarding the way in which limited or partial sets of data have been used to support the hypothesis. The use of the clinical service framework, as we shall see, highlights and illuminates the problem.

We shall here suggest specific areas of research focusing on the emergence of mental health problems among Hispanic populations. In this connection, the relationship between migration and mental health is important because a significant number of Hispanics in the United States are first-generation residents and the literature consistently asserts an association between migration and stressful experiences.[21] While working on a program of comparative field studies focusing upon the impact of migration on mental health in the greater New York City area, the Hispanic Research Center developed a series of theoretical formulations relevant to this complex relationship. First, we became aware of the importance of directly confronting the issue of Hispanic diversity in order to avoid stereotyping Hispanic groups into one homogeneous category. Hispanic populations differ from each other in size, socioeconomic status, residential settlement patterns, the structure of their intergroup relations, and the historical and psychological conditions associated with migration.[22] Thus, Hispanic diversity in relation to appropriate comparison groups, provides an opportunity for examining the complex linkage between migration and mental health. Because Hispanic diversity has been almost totally ignored in current analyses of the issues and problems of Hispanics in the United States, we present, in the appendix at the end of this volume, an overview of the socioeconomic characteristics, social welfare problems and assimila-

8

tion of Hispanic groups in one urban setting, New York City.

Second, we confronted the issue of selecting the dimensions of mental health to be studied. We chose anxiety, depression and self-esteem since these dimensions not only are centrally relevant to prevailing notions of mental health and illness[23] but also are the most frequent problems presented by Hispanics at a New York City community mental health clinic.[24] Thus, research was designed to capitalize methodologically upon the facts of Hispanic diversity while focusing upon the Hispanic immigrant's problems of anxiety, depression, and self-esteem.

We then faced the necessity of developing theoretical formulations which not only identify, but also systematically interrelate the complex processes associated with the migration experience to mental health. Attempts at such efforts have provided lists or classes of variables, but the lists themselves do not satisfy the need for organized theoretical formulations of the processes linking migration to mental health.[25] To develop such formulations, we turned to bodies of literature other than those which attempt to link migration with mental health. Specifically, we found that primary stresses or strains are locked into three basic components of the migration experience of disadvantaged immigrants: insertion at the bottom of the social stratification heap, disturbances in the family life cycle, and acculturative problems.

Migration from one culture to another inevitably inserts the person into the host society's socioeconomic system. Immigrants, therefore, are rendered differentially vulnerable to stress according to their position in the system. Most Hispanic immigrants are economically disadvantaged. The strain of this lower socioeconomic position is doubly confounded not only by pressures stemming from fluctuations in the economy which disproportionately affect those of lower socioeconomic status, but also by the pressures associated with the experience of downward mobility.[26] A common finding among immigrants is that their occupations immediately after migration represent a step down from the jobs they left in the society of origin. Thus, in examining the migration experience of Hispanics, attention must be given to the environmental pressures which result from their insertion into the host society's socioeconomic system, the changes in such pressures stemming from fluctuations in the economy, downward mobility, and the resulting, often severe, adaptational requirements imposed upon them.

Hispanic immigrants undergo more than insertion into a different stratification system. Modifications in the family life cycle also occur as a result of migration. This is important because research has shown that emotional problems are associated with the family life cycle as indicated by marital status, the presence of children, and living arrangements.[27] Migration can alter the family life cycle by separating close relatives, postponing marriage and family formation, and creating family disruption. Alterations in economic careers and family life cycles occur to non-migrants, internal migrants, and migrants between cultures; however, they are likely to be more severe and problematic for the latter. Regardless of the degree of severity, alterations in basic dimensions of the family life cycle must be examined if we are to understand the impact of the migration experience on the mental health of Hispanics. Such alterations often entail undesirable changes in the immigrant's life space.

Formulations based upon position in the socioeconomic system and alterations in the family life cycle are structurally oriented. They must be enlarged to include cultural factors if we are to comprehend the facts of Hispanic migration. The major concept here is acculturation which refers to the complex process whereby the behaviors and attitudes of the migrant group change toward the dominant group as a result of exposure to a cultural system that is significantly different. Although there is no general agreement regarding the major components of acculturation, Padilla notes that there are five which are repeatedly mentioned in the acculturation literature: language familiarity and usage, cultural heritage, ethnic pride, interethnic distance, and perceived discrimination.[28] Some studies have related measures of acculturation to mental health.[29] These studies have given scant attention to the multiplicity of dimensions underlying acculturation as evidenced by Padilla's five components. Regardless of such operational problems, however, the data on the relevance of acculturation to mental health are more than suggestive, even though the relationship between the two is likely to be more complex than originally envisioned.[30] On a broad scale, studies are needed which specify the interrelationship of acculturation with the structural components of the migration experience, namely, the insertion of immigrants into different levels of the host society's stratificational system and alterations in the family life cycle.

Insertion into the host society's stratificational system, alterations in the family life cycle, and the obstacles embedded in acculturation are prisms through which the migration experience is refracted. In less metaphorical and more direct terms, each of the three components of the migration experience could represent a more or less enduring source of primary strain impinging upon the Hispanic immigrant. To convey the point more clearly and forcefully, we point to the case of first-generation Puerto Rican families the Hispanic Research Center has studied in the South Bronx.[31] Inserted into the host society at the very bottom of the urban stratification heap, they are vulnerable to economic downturns which bring rising unemployment. Families are disrupted in the move to the mainland or in the return migration to the island-home in the search for economic survival. The proportion of single-parent households in the Puerto Rican community has continued to increase in recent years.[32] Language differences and discriminatory practices exclude their participation in the more rewarding institutional structures. Such external events have their internal, subjective correlatives. In-depth interviews with such families have documented their members' feelings that, in the hierarchy of groups, they are at the bottom of the ladder; that society consistently favors all other ethnic groups; and that they are excluded from sources of well-being common to other groups. The degree to which such strains are actually experienced, we believe, varies according to the facts of Hispanic diversity; that is, among the Hispanic immigrant groups. Although the Hispanic groups are economically disadvantaged compared to the non-Hispanic population, the degree of disadvantage varies considerably. Compared to Mexican Americans and Puerto Ricans, Cubans and "other Hispanics" have relatively high educational attainment, occupational status, and earnings. These differences are reflected in figures on family income. The average family incomes of Cubans and "other Hispanics" are 85 percent and 80 percent, respectively, of that of non-Hispanic families. That of Mexicans is 72 percent, while that of Puerto Ricans is 46 percent of the non-Hispanic family standard. At this level of aggregation, the average incomes of all Hispanic families are low, but the differences among Hispanic groups exceed those between some Hispanic and non-Hispanic groups.[33]

Data on family life cycle variables, including marital status and prevalence of female-headed families and acculturation variables such as English language proficiency, also convey a portrait of Hispanics being disadvantaged in comparison to the majority population. In addition, these data document the less well-known fact of diversity among Hispanic groups. For example, the prevalence of female-headed families among Puerto Ricans is more than double that of "other Hispanic" groups, and the English-language proficiency of first-generation Mexicans is considerably lower than that of Puerto Ricans, Central/South Americans and "other Spanish" persons born outside the United States.[34] To repeat, such diversity provides the opportunity for examining the complex linkage between migration and mental health.

The relationship between primary economic, familial and acculturation strains and mental health or illness is likely to be complex, for the very same reason that the relationship between stress, the mediators of stress, and the manifestations of stress is complicated.[35] It could be, for example, that the primary strains embedded in the migration experience affect the immigrant's mental health status directly or immediately. Or, it could be that their impact upon mental health is mediated through psychological, demographic, and institutional variables characterizing the immigrant.[36] Or both could be true. Or the patterns could even be more complicated. The determination of the most appropriate theoretical model, however, rests upon the conclusions of well-designed research.

The theoretical formulations presented here favor the view that recent life-event changes along with socially supportive indigenous institutions intervene between migration-induced primary strains and the immigrant's psychological status. Let us explain the reserach background of this idea. In the Rogler-Hollingshead study[37] of schizophrenia among families living in the slums and public housing developments of San Juan, Puerto Rico, the families were desperately poor and the psychiatrically diagnosed schizophrenics never had experienced professional mental health care. The study demonstrated retrospectively that during the year prior to the perceived onset of illness the schizophrenic persons experienced many more problems than a comparable group of psychiatrically "well" persons. The schizophrenic persons experienced more of the following: economic difficulties, physical deprivations; conflict with spouses, other members of the family, and neighbors; physical illnesses; and a lack of understanding from other persons. Briefly, they felt bombarded by a multiplicity of seemingly unending problems despite their struggle to solve them by every means available. Since the publication of the book reporting the study's findings, a modest legacy of research has demonstrated that the magnitude of recent life-event changes is linked to depression,[38] anxiety,[39] schizophrenia,[40] psychiatric hospitalization,[41] suicide attempts,[42] and general symptomatology.[43] Children having problems in school, adults having clashes with their bosses, undesired residential moves, and the experience of being criminally victimized are examples of life events. It seems more than likely that the frequent occurrence of such events, particularly those which are culturally undesirable,[44] is related to psychological disorders.

The concept of recent life events, we believe, can shed light on the complexities of the migration-mental health connection. To do this, a distinction must be maintained between the primary strains embedded in the migration experience and the discrete recent events measured by life-event inventories, although both call attention to experiential changes in the immigrant's life. The strains resulting from being inserted into a disadvantageous position in the socioeconomic structure, family life-cycle disruptions, and acculturative problems represent persistent and difficult adaptational requirements in the lives of immigrants. As Pearlin and his associates note with respect to the concept of role strain, which is analogous to the concept of migration-induced primary strains, such strains are "especially inimical to self-esteem and mastery because they represent testimony to one's lack of success."[45] Primary strains are an affront to the immigrant's concept of self.

Having recommended the importance of maintaining a distinction between primary strains and life-event changes, we argue now that migration-induced primary strains give rise to many unfavorable life-event changes. The inability to speak the host society's language, the disruption of family bonds, the exposure to repeated cycles of unemployment, all have a reverberating impact upon the immigrant's daily life events. Thus, it could be that migration-induced primary strains condition the appearance of recent life-event changes, that there is a sequence from the first to the second which progressively escalates the Hispanic migrant's exposure to stress. This proposition parallels but is not the equivalent of the main conclusions of research already cited,[46] that increases in unemployment at the aggregate level increase stressful life events. Such events, as we have seen, bear a stable relationship to a variety of psychological disorders.

Our final argument is that the impact of primary strains upon psychological disorders, whether manifested through life events or not, is undoubtedly mediated by a variety of factors. Thus, some research has concluded that personality factors, such as the degree or extent to which persons are "hardy," mediate the stress-illness relationship.[47] Other research has focused on the person's coping styles in modifying situations creating stress, changing the meaning of problems to reduce their threat, or in the management of stress symptoms.[48] Indeed, the issue of mediating factors in the stress-illness relationship is so much at the core of social psychiatry as to invite programmatically organized comparative research. But the research would be incomplete if, in focusing upon Hispanic groups, it did not attend to the social supports rooted in indigenous cultural organizations.

To illustrate this point let us return to the Rogler-Hollingshead study conducted in Puerto Rico.[49] This research was the first to document empirically the psychotherapeutic functions of spiritualism in relation to the problems of the mentally ill. The study demonstrated that among persons at the bottom of the San Juan stratification heap, the institution of spiritualism is the most prevalent form of social organization outside the family which helps persons experiencing emotional problems and mental illness. Subsequent studies have shown that spiritualism as a form of folk psychiatry retains its vitality in New York City.[50] Complicated historical and cultural factors have shaped spiritualism's explicit therapeutic focus upon emotional or psychological problems.[51] But other types of indigenous cultural organizations which do not have such an explicit and highly institutionalized focus upon psychological problems also qualify as socially supportive. The important point, as Pearlin notes, is that social support depends upon more than the extensiveness of interpersonal relations and frequency of interaction. It requires intimate communication and the presence of solidarity and trust.[52]

If such supportive organizations provide alternative resources for coping with emotional problems, could they not perform a preventive function for those immigrants who are not yet experiencing such problems? This question is, of course, a variant of Emile Durkheim's proposition that psychic unity is a function of group cohesion.[53] Integration into cohesive indigenous organizations may immediately and directly reduce the risk of emotional distress. Or, it could be, that integration into such organizations mitigates the impact of external stresses, whether their source be in migration-induced primary strains, in unfavorable recent life events, or in both. Research may in fact support several alternative formulations. The ways in which indigenous Hispanic organizations perform a preventive or protective function are likely to be complicated and subject to variations across Hispanic groups.

In developing these formulations, we have drawn from the rapidly accumulating research literature focusing upon the triadic relationship between stress, supportive social organizations, and psychological disorder. We are aware that this literature has been repeatedly subjected to critical examination and that many methodological problems have been uncovered in the conceptualization and measurement of stress, in the procedural

13

creation of tautologous relationships between stress and emotional problems, in the meaning and measurement of mediating or supportive patterns, in the temporal sequence of relevant variables, and, indeed, in the measurement errors associated with the assessment of mental illness, to mention but a few. Many such problems remain unsolved, but research in this area also exhibits a surprising vitality in the self-conscious efforts being made to improve procedures and ideas.

As a concrete illustration of such research relevant to the first phase of our conceptual framework, we present a study now under way in the Hispanic Research Center. Using retrospective life-history data from a 1981 survey of Dominican and Colombian immigrants in New York City, the study[54] analyzes the epidemiological processes associated with variations in their anxiety level in an attempt to specify the role that concrete social structures and processes play in mediating the psychological status of individuals. In pursuing this goal, the processes of immigration, integration, and acculturation are related to the family life-cycle and the process of occupational change.

The study views migration as a process involving the interaction of a particular type of residential move with a set of life-cycle and career conditions. Upon arrival in the host country, individuals may function as temporary visitors or they may become, or move toward becoming, permanent settlers. This settlement process will be influenced by factors such as economic integration and success, social integration into local social structures, be they Hispanic or North American, and acculturation. What is happening in each of these dimensions will influence anxiety level in some way. Consequently, the study explicitly seeks to identify mechanisms within the migration-integration-acculturation processes which affect mental health directly or indirectly through their impact on factors such as socioeconomic status, marital stability and household composition.

One of the focal points of analysis is the identification of differences in marital status that produce changes in anxiety status. An intriguing preliminary finding has been that for the Dominicans and Colombians studied, factors associated with migration, settlement, and acculturation appear to be better predictors of anxiety than structured life stresses (economic stress, social isolation, and parental responsibilities). Knowledge of English, cognitive acculturation (awareness of basic facts about the U.S. environment), and years in the United States, for example, proved to be the major determinants of anxiety and of anxiety differentials by marital status category.

Kessler[55] has demonstrated that the well-established negative relationship between socioeconomic status and mental illness requires considerably more attention than it has received to date. The effect of socioeconomic status on mental health varies across categories such as sex and employment status. Preliminary analysis has produced results consistent with those reported by Kessler. For example, income is more important for men, and education is more important for women. As in the case of the analysis of marital status, immigration and acculturation factors appear more important than socio-economic factors, and they too differ in importance across basic social categories. Acculturation measures are significantly more important predictors of anxiety among women than men (although men score higher on basic indicators of acculturation).

In sum, the study addresses a core issue in the search for determinants of variations in anxiety status. That issue is the role that social structure and process play in influencing individual psychological functioning. In pursuing this goal, the research extends current work focusing on socioeconomic status, marital status, and sex differentials. Pervading these efforts is a systematic evaluation of the impacts of the processes of migration, integration, and acculturation on anxiety status.

Thus, the first phase of the framework focuses upon the conditions associated with emerging mental health problems, recommends psychiatric epidemiology as the indicated method in the initiation of this phase, and calls attention to the importance of the migration experience which involves insertion into a new stratificational system, disruption in the life cycle, and acculturation problems creating strains for the migrant population.

# Phase 2:
# HELP-SEEKING BEHAVIOR

Hispanic utilization of mental health facilities is the central problem of research in the framework's second phase. Admission rates, taken as evidence of utilization of mental health facilities, are based upon the proportion of users of a particular mental health facility, or a number of such facilities, who are members of a Hispanic group in relation to that group's proportionate size in the population or the relevant catchment area. When the first proportion is smaller than the second proportion, the group is said to "underutilize"; when the first proportion is larger than the second, it is said to "overutilize." Admission rates have also been used to make intergroup (ethnic or racial) comparisons in determining over- and under-utilization. Research findings based upon either procedure generally point to the Hispanics' underutilization of mental health facilities, although there are, as we shall see, important exceptions to the pattern.

There are two theories which proffer explanations of the Hispanics' underutilization of mental health facilities: alternative resource theory and barrier theory. The theory of alternative resources explains underutilization in terms of the indigenous Hispanic social organizations serving as therapeutic alternatives to the official mental health agency system. The explicit argument is that Hispanics with psychological problems first turn to proximate and culturally familiar indigenous organizations and, if no satisfactory solution of the problem is attained, then, as a last resort, they turn to mental health facilities. The theory of barriers, on the other hand, explains underutilization as a result of structural impediments of professional mental health care. The class of variables or factors each theory utilizes for explanatory purposes also differs, as we shall see below. However, although the two theories differ in these respects, they can be integrated into a more comprehensive and dynamic explanation of Hispanic underutilization.

To begin with, research on the topic of utilization is scarce, and arguments relevant to true prevalence and patterns of utilization tend to be intertwined. However, a number of studies do conclude that Hispanics tend

17

to underutilize the mental health system. Bachrach's study[56] of Hispanic utilization of mental health services concluded that Hispanics were under-represented in their admissions to inpatient psychiatric units of state and county hospitals throughout the United States. This study is important because it attempted to compile national data on Hispanic mental health. Since that time, several additional national surveys have been administered by the NIMH with the results generally agreeing with those of Bachrach. Hispanics have been found to underutilize outpatient psychiatric services, private psychiatric hospitals, and the psychiatric services of non-public, non-federal general hospitals.[57] (At the same time, Hispanics were found to overutilize the inpatient psychiatric services of public non-federal general hospitals.) In a more localized study, Karno and Edgerton[58] found that in 1966, Mexican Americans comprised only 3.3 percent of the resident population of California's state hospitals for the mentally ill, at a time when Mexican Americans comprised 9 to 10 percent of California's population. The studies generally support the hypothesis that Mexican Americans under-utilize mental health facilities.

In contrast, New York City's Puerto Rican population has been found to have higher rates of reported psychiatric admissions than other ethnic groups in the city. Malzberg,[59] in his analysis of the first admissions of all New York City residents to New York State psychiatric hospitals for the period 1949-1951, concluded that the admission rate was considerably higher for Puerto Ricans than for non-Puerto Ricans. In addition, 58 percent of all Puerto Rican first admissions were diagnosed as schizophrenic, compared to 29 percent for non-Puerto Ricans. Fitzpatrick and Gould[60] replicated this work based upon 1967 hospital admission figures for New York State, concluding that there exists an even greater disparity in the rates of reported first admissions and diagnosed schizophrenia between Puerto Ricans and the general population than was observed by Malzberg.

Several studies using administratively collected data provide additional information on admission rates of Puerto Ricans in New York City. In a study of service delivery to mentally ill residents of the Metropolitan Community Mental Health Center catchment area from 1970 to 1973,[61] the admission rates for non-Hispanic whites were considerably lower than those for blacks and Puerto Ricans: 251.6 Puerto Rican outpatients per 10,000 Puerto Ricans in the population; 158.7 per 10,000 blacks; and 53.6 per 10,000 whites. Similarly, for inpatients, Puerto Rican admission rates were twice those for whites. It was found that a significant portion of this discrepancy was the result of the practice of upper-middle class whites to use facilities outside of the catchment area, while the Puerto Rican population of the area was found to use the local facilities to a greater extent than did either black or white non-Hispanic residents.

Another study conducted at the same time in the Bellevue catchment area of New York City[62] found that admission rates for Puerto Ricans and blacks were higher than those for whites. However, black and Puerto Rican clients had fewer outpatient visits per admission than did white clients, suggesting a differential treatment profile for minorities. The basis for this differential may lie partially in the client's attitude toward these services, but it may also be the result of the administrative policies of the facilities, the lack of bilingual personnel, and the absence of culturally sensitive treatment modalities.

Alers,[63] also using New York City figures for admission to all local community mental health and retardation facilities, reported that the total admission rate for Puerto Ricans was approximately twice the rate for non-Hispanics. At the same time, the data demonstrated that the rates for whites were lower than for Puerto Ricans and blacks in all major diagnostic categories.

Finally, Canino et al.[64] constructed a mental health profile of Puerto Rican children, relative to other New York City children, based upon the New York State Department of Mental Hygiene's admission form (MS-5). (Although this admission form is the best source of data in New York for group mental health patterns, the authors caution that there are serious methodological problems associated with this source.) The data show that the rates of reported admission interviews for Puerto Rican and black children are considerably higher than those for non-Hispanic white children, with the highest rates found among Puerto Rican children. In comparison to white children, Puerto Rican children demonstrated a higher frequency of symptoms in the categories of sleep and articulation problems, physical problems, inadequate intellectual development, problems with others in school, anxiety and fear, anger and belligerence, agitation and hyperactivity, and antisocial activities.

It is more than a matter of passing interest — and perhaps an issue for future research — that the research literature tends to characterize Mexican Americans as underutilizers and Puerto Ricans as overutilizers, although one study[65] found the rate of treatment of Puerto Ricans to be 3.5 times lower than that for blacks. Does the difference in utilization between the two Hispanic groups reflect higher prevalence rates of mental distress among Puerto Ricans? Or are the barriers to utilization more formidable for Mexican Americans than for Puerto Ricans? Or are there indigenous social organizations in the two Hispanic groups which are creating such differences? We can raise these questions but we cannot answer them: when placed in the context of the clinical service model's first phase, admission rates are necessary but not sufficient in arriving at a meaningful and appropriate conclusion regarding over- and underutilization. Thus, Puerto Ricans characterized as overutilizers, because of their proportionately higher admissions, may be underutilizers relative to their mental health needs. Admission rates, therefore, must be seen in relation to the true prevalence rates of mental health problems in the specific group. Conclusions relevant to over- and underutilization would then be premised upon the magnitude of differences between the two rates, and the admission rate would be expected to be consistently less than the prevalence rate. The larger the disparity between the two rates, the more the underutilization. Research to provide data for the computation of such rates is needed desperately if we are to arrive at sound policy decisions regarding the Hispanics' utilization of mental health service facilities. Such research must be placed in two broader contexts: (1) persons at the lower end of the socioeconomic scale tend, in general, to underutilize mental health facilities,[66] and (2) based on admission data, Hispanics underutilize all medical facilities in general, even including dentists.[67]

## Alternative Resource Theory

The picture becomes more complicated and the need for research even greater when we recognize the fact that in addition to the official mental health agencies and bureaucracies, there are a myriad of informal, primary group structures coping with the psychological problems of Hispanics. How well such primary group structures function in coping with emotional distress in comparison to the official mental health system is a moot point. Simply put, we do not know.

But the issue deserves attention in the interest of improving the effectiveness of bureaucratic responses to problems of mental health, and also because it is intrinsically important to the clinical service framework being developed here. In fact, primary group structures may well mediate the relationship between emotional distress and contact with the agency system — the beginning and the end of the framework's second phase — and thus be centrally relevant to the varying linkages between true prevalence and admission rates. Historically, the national movement to deliver mental health services on a mass, democratic, bureaucratic scale dates back to the rise of the community mental health movement in the 1960's. Prior to that, state and local efforts to deliver adequate mental health care to economically disadvantaged populations, such as Hispanics, were feeble indeed both in purpose and in impact, and there is hardly need to mention the wretched history of psychiatric asylums in the United States. In contrast, primary group structures relevant to mental health care — the family, the circle of friends and acquaintances, the Hispanic *compadrazgo* (coparent) system, religious and spiritualist groups — are an integral part of the Hispanic culture and function alongside the official agency system. Perhaps one of the most important research and policy issues forming part of the clinical service framework's second phase is the seemingly complicated and as yet unknown system of interrelationships between the experience of psychological distress, contact with help-giving agencies, and such primary structures. Now we shall return to this issue.

The assumption of most of the relevant literature is that Hispanics, as compared to their mental health needs, turn to mental health agencies less frequently than other groups. Hence there is a problem of underutilization. As mentioned before, alternative resource theory and barrier theory emerge as the two explanations of this problem. To view the problem from the perspective of alternative resources is to view it in the context of social organizations. The psychologically afflicted person's help-seeking efforts are seen in the context of institutionally organized interpersonal relations and networks. The person is seen in relation to the family, the circle of friends, neighbors and acquaintances, the *compadrazgo* system, the indigenous folk healing institutions, and the mental health agency system. The broadest question to be posed, consequently, is how does the interrelationship among these institutional groupings affect the person's help-seeking efforts. Is getting help from the family likely to decrease the probability of the afflicted person's seeking help from friends or folk healers or the mental health agency system? Do such institutional groupings represent alternative sources of help or are they conjoined in the provision of help? In comparison to other groups, to what extent do Hispanics use such institutional groupings? Does the pattern of use from one resource to another differ across ethnic group and social class levels? The literature on these questions is confusing, but its size nonetheless attests to the importance ascribed to social organization — and, hence, to alternative resource theory — in understanding patterns of mental health utilization. In keeping with this presentation's objective, we repeat that we do not seek a comprehensive review of the alternative resource literature. Rather, we attempt some observations of the research literature which are specifically relevant to the clinical service framework being presented here.

The family is the foremost institution in Hispanic culture seen as relevant to underutilization. The prevailing view is well presented by Hoppe and Heller:

> Familism is a positive form of social organization that facilitates their (Hispanics') adaptation to the conditions of marginal (objectively alienated) existence and its subjectively alienating consequences. Family ties serve supportive and protective functions against the risk of failure, economic loss, embarrassment, and vulnerability to criticism encountered in the broader society. Such ties serve as a "buffer" between the objectively alienated Mexican American and the Anglo middle-class society.[68]

It is understandable why the family, in the context of the underutilization issue, is viewed almost exclusively as a supportive, help-giving system, since the giving and receiving of help is an integral component of familial bonds.[69] But the generalizing of this view to encompass all issues relevant to mental health creates romantic stereotypes which are scientifically counter-productive and cloud the possibility of studying the family as a source of mental distress. Not all that goes on in Hispanic families is supportive, harmonious, and consensually based. As in other groups, there are also conflict and dissension, bitter recrimination, and violence — a view which is consistent, for example, with the rapid increase of single parent households among New York City's Puerto Ricans.[70] The increasing problems besetting the Puerto Rican family are also suggested by the rising number of divorces in relation to marriages among New York City Puerto Ricans: in 1960 there was one person divorced for every 24 persons married, and in 1970, one person divorced for every 15 persons married.[71]

To some researchers, the major difference between Anglos and Mexican Americans in help-seeking behavior is to be found in the latter group's seeking of help primarily from the family rather than from friends.[72] The difference should be seen, however, in the Mexican American's more exclusive dependence upon the family for help,[73] and the Anglo's disposition to seek help from friends, neighbors, and coworkers. Conclusions on this point differ, however, as the following indicate:

> Mexican Americans as a whole deal with emotional problems in a variety of ways. They tend to know about the neighborhood mental health clinics but these are not utilized to any great extent. Instead, Mexican Americans depend upon physicians, relatives, friends, and religious practitioners for treatment.[74]

> Mexican Americans' main resource, on the other hand, is their extended kin network; there is relatively little support derived from other informal sources.[75]

Although the importance of the family is reaffirmed, the importance of friends or informal sources as help givers remains inconclusive.

Much of the literature on the family in Puerto Rico parallels the findings on Mexican Americans. Rogler and Hollingshead[76] documented how families living in the most impoverished neighborhoods and public housing developments in San Juan, Puerto Rico, enmesh their members in a system of help-giving exchanges. The system incorporates the nuclear family into the extended family, because mutual help criss-crosses blood and affinal relationships. Mutual help, in fact, has the force of a sacred obligatory norm: it is sustained by the double edge of guilt and gratitude. That is, not to help a relative in need evokes feelings of sinful guilt: in turn, to be helped by a relative induces feelings of gratitude. The norm applies through time because the person is bound permanently to his or her family of origin; and it applies through space, because relatives who are separated by geographical distance behave in accordance with the norm. The norm's impact is evident in the finding that at the time the study's data were collected, 88 percent of the nuclear families were either giving or receiving material goods in contacts with their relatives. The type of help given is linked to sex roles in the family: the women provide family-centered, socioemotional support; the men, the type of help associated with their instrumental roles of linking the family to institutions outside the family.

The findings are not unique. Many studies have documented the family's essential role in the institutional character of Puerto Rican society. The family is central to the island's stratification system, social mobility patterns, and the transition from an agrarian to an industrial society;[77] it mediates between the economic base of communities and socialization patterns;[78] it shapes the social experiences which accrue from socialization;[79] it is the main context of economic consumption;[80] it is an important repository of modernizing impulses to social change;[81] it binds together reciprocal patterns of help in facilitating rural-to-urban migration and adaptation;[82] it mitigates the implementation of middle-class rules in urban public housing developments;[83] it extends itself into the ritual coparent system of *compadrazgo* to enlarge the scope of its social security function;[84] it is the object of devotion in an overarching system of cultural values;[85] it is the primary setting for the care of the mentally ill;[86] and it even shapes the character of entrepreneurial activities through its system of paternalistic relationships.[87] Despite rapid social change, Puerto Rican society at the root cultural level still centers upon the family and its functions.

Very little is known about the Puerto Rican family in New York City,[88] particularly about its vitality as a help-giving system; how geographical and social mobility affects the system; and how it changes, if at all, from the first to the second generation which now comprises about half of the Puerto Rican population in the city. Most speculations, supported by patches of data, favor the view that migration and acculturation are altering the extended family system.[89]

In spite of the theoretical and empirical importance of intergenerational change in the analysis of ethnic groups in American society, little research has focused upon intergenerational change in acculturation within the family. One Hispanic Research Center project[90] has attempted to analyze acculturation based upon an intensive study of 100 intergenerationally linked Puerto Rican nuclear families in metropolitan New York and adjoining states. It posed the following research questions: Are there significant differences in acculturation between parents and children? When each generation is taken separately, what factors influence acculturation in inter-generationally linked parents and children?

In answering these questions, it was found that parents and children showed expected differences in acculturation. Children were less likely to speak Spanish and reported less language ability in Spanish but greater language ability in English and less of a preference for Puerto Rican culture than their parents. In addressing the factors explaining acculturation, the study established the importance of education. Education was significantly related to language spoken with family, friends and neighbors, mass media language usage, knowledge of English and knowledge of Spanish for both parents; but was unrelated to subjective ethnic affiliation for both parents. In contrast, education was significantly related only to knowledge of English for children. Both education and age of arrival had significant independent

23

effects upon the acculturation of mothers, fathers, and children, and child's education and age of arrival were significantly and independently related to changes in acculturation within the family. Acculturation, it was found, cannot be equated simply with birthplace of respondent and his or her ancestors, but varies according to age of exposure to the new set of influences in the host environment. Although the children's acculturation was significantly greater than that of their parents, the pattern of children's responses suggested a movement to biculturalism as opposed to complete assimilation. Thus, the study is the first step in the direction of providing systematic knowledge on a topic which has not been directly researched: intergenerational family processes in the stateside Puerto Rican community.

Similarly, little is known about the role of neighbors and friends as help-givers among New York City's Puerto Ricans. In yesterday's agrarian Puerto Rico, the pattern of mutual aid extended beyond the kin group to include neighbors and friends. The survival of a person or a family often depended upon the fulfillment of such obligations embedded in tradition. Thus, during the Great Depression, in a community study conducted in a small town located in the central mountainous interior of the island, a sociologist presented the problem of how "it is possible for a family to live on fifty cents a day which is earned only three or four months a year, even where a little money may be earned occasionally at odd jobs."[91] The solution given was that "the survival of a large number of families is dependent upon the aid received from neighbors." Out of 26 typically poor families which were studied, 20 were either giving or receiving help from friends and neighbors. Such exchanges involved labor among workers in agriculture, and even the adoption of children of deceased parents by friends and neighbors. A subsequent study by an anthropologist of a traditional coffee municipality demonstrated that the fulfillment of reciprocal obligations between families is so deeply embedded in the ideals and practices of the culture that a person's perception of his or her economic standard of living includes the expenses entailed in obligations to neighbors.[92] Other studies suggest, however, that social changes in Puerto Rico are attenuating the traditional bonds of help between neighbors and friends,[93] and that in San Juan the neighboring bond is weakest among families at the bottom of the stratification heap.[94] With little research-based knowledge, speculations favor the view that in New York City such traditional bonds are also attenuated.

Another supportive network commonly cited as important in traditional Hispanic culture is the *compadrazgo* (coparent) system. Along with material, moral, and spiritual responsibilities of the godparents toward the godchild, functioning as a form of indigenous social security, *compadrazgo* binds the godparents and the godchild's parents into a pattern of mutual respect and help. Fitzpatrick[95] states that Puerto Ricans in this system "constitute a network of ritual kinship, as serious and important as that of natural kinship, around a person or a group." As a traditional idealized system, the statement is true. However, Rogler and Hollingshead's[96] previously cited study conducted in Puerto Rico found little evidence of a viable, help-giving *compadrazgo* system; in turn, ongoing research at Fordham University's Hispanic Research Center, focusing upon New York City's Puerto Ricans, shows little improvement by coparents in help-giving exchanges. The same appears to be the case among Mexican Americans.[97] Unless new and more convincing evidence is produced by research, the *compadrazgo* system among Puerto Ricans and Mexican Americans can more appropriately be viewed as having essentially ceremonial meaning, a ritualized cultural form defining respectful *"usted"* (formal) relationships between the relevant parties.

Perhaps the most disputed area in the question of alternative sources of support for Hispanics is the role of spiritualist and *curandero,* the folk healers in Hispanic culture. The subject has received a remarkable amount of attention, ever since the Rogler and Hollingshead study[98] first documented empirically the psychotherapeutic functions of spiritualist sessions in relation to the problems of the mentally ill. The study demonstrated that among persons at the bottom of the San Juan stratification heap, the institution of spiritualism is the most prevalent form of social organization outside the family which helps persons experiencing emotional stress and mental illness.[99] As an ideology, spiritualism assumes an invisible world of good and bad spirits who intrude into human affairs and can be employed by mediums who have developed psychic faculties *(facultades)* to cure illness, arbitrate personal disputes, and explain events incongruous with common sense. As an institution, spiritualism is directly interwoven into the trials and tribulations of persons in the San Juan slums and public housing projects; the medium provides spiritualistic interpretations which are simple, credible, and given in a setting free of the stigma associated with psychiatric treatment at hospitals or clinics. In Puerto Rico, persons of modest means almost invariably turn to spiritualism before contacting a psychiatrist or mental health worker. Descriptive accounts of Puerto Rican life in New York City show that in this setting spiritualism as a form of folk psychiatry retains its vitality and functions,[100] and that it converges with the eclectic Christian, African, and West Indian religious practice of *santeria.*

Assertions have been made that folk healers may be more in harmony with Hispanic views of mental illess than traditional therapists,[101] and that therapist and folk healers should work together[102] under some circumstances or whenever feasible.[103] Such proposals, it would seem, assume that folk healing practices are deeply and pervasively rooted in the culture, so that their incorporation into the clinical setting represents nothing more than the extension of indigenous culture into the official mental health system. But the question of how often and how pervasively folk healers are used, and the attitudes of Hispanics toward folk healers has not been clearly answered, in particular with respect to Mexican Americans. Thus, where one study finds that most people would not use folk healers,[104] another finds Mexican

Americans willing to accept both drugs from a psychiatrist and herbal medicine from a healer.[105] Or, folk healing may be a resource that is used when professional help is not available;[106] a treatment that may be used in conjunction with traditional therapy;[107] or a relatively unimportant factor.[108] One reason offered for this mixed picture is that Mexican Americans may be ashamed of ancient folk healing in the American context and will not admit that they have recourse to it.[109] A second suggestion is that resorting to folk healing is primarily a lower class phenomenon in rural areas, and may change in urban and economically advanced communities.[110] On the other hand, the literature that is available for Puerto Ricans — as mentioned before — seems to indicate a somewhat widespread use of folk healing. Puerto Ricans often intertwine their use of spiritualists with therapists;[111] and in many Puerto Rican communities, spiritualists are reported to be more numerous than mental health professionals.[112]

In sum, the social organization enmeshing Hispanics — the family, neighbors and friends, the fictive coparent system and indigenous folk healers — represents alternative resources for coping with emotional problems. To some researchers,[113] these organizational resources represent the most potent explanation for the underutilization of mental health facilities. The explicit argument is that Hispanics first turn to such organizations which are proximate and familiar, and, if no satisfactory solution to the emotional problem results, then as a last resort, they turn to mental health clinics. Two implications derive from this statement. First, if we take the broader meaning of the concept of underutilization — high mental health need conjoined with low utilization — to be factually correct, then Hispanic culture is endowed with organizational strength in coping with the psychological problems of its members. The strength is being utilized to resolve or contain many of the Hispanics' psychological problems after they arise without resorting to professional mental health practitioners. Second, despite such strength, the indigenous social organizations are not capable of fully mitigating the impact of stresses arising from the Hispanics' disadvantaged and marginated status; thus, their high mental health needs. Two functions, therefore, should be kept separate: the indigenous system's capacity to keep psychological problems from arising and its capacity to treat or contain such problems once they have arisen.

If we demand hard, systematic evidence in support of such implications — evidence based upon an organized program of well-executed research — the demand cannot be fulfilled at present because the available research simply does not suffice. Indeed, it has barely begun. We need programmatically organized research focusing upon he triadic interrelationship between mental health needs, patterns of social utilization, and the mediating indigenous social organizations, and how this system of interrelationships is affected by cultural factors such as language differences, the Hispanics' values and their perceptions of mental illness. We believe that this focus is at the core of the clinical service sequence's second phase, the process leading to contacts with mental health agencies. Soon we shall return to the research recommendations to discuss how alternative resource theory fits into the clincial service research framework.

## Barrier Theory

The prevailing explanations for Hispanic underutilization are couched, first, in terms of indigenous social organizations which serve as alternative resources to mental health facilities, the theory just discussed; and, second, in terms of barriers which keep Hispanics away from such facilities. To accentuate the differences between the two explanations, we need only conjecture on the research implications of conceiving indigenous social organizations as "barriers" to agency mental health care, since the alternative resource theory states that such organizations do keep Hispanics away from the mental health system. To accept such a conjecture is. to accept an assumption of the absolute, therapeutic preeminence of the mental health agency system; in effect, it is to postulate that the official mental health practitioner commands an exclusive monopoly over therapeutic-relevant experience, skills, and knowledge. According to this argument, anything that keeps the afflicted person away from the agency system or delays contact with the system is, effectively, a barrier to appropriate mental health care. When stated explicitly, the argument is patently unacceptable. The development and implementation of the therapeutic community modality after World War II, and the development of the community mental health movement in the 1960's are squarely premised upon assumptions which attribute therapeutic gains to a variety of human interactions, not just those which entail contact with professional mental health workers. Although false, the argument is stated explicitly to counterbalance the tendency to see the problem of Hispanic agency underutilization in a narrow or provincial manner, stripped away from considerations regarding the functions of indigenous cultural resources. Within the broader framework we seek to develop, equally relevant research questions could be raised regarding those barriers which keep persons away from the therapeutic benefits of the indigenous social organizations.

Nonetheless, it is a fact that the research literature, consistently adhering to the mental health agency perspective, formulates the theory only in terms of barriers which keep Hispanics away from such agencies or from professional mental health practitioners. What the theory basically states is that there are many structural incongruities between the assumptions and characteristics of Hispanic culture and those of the mental health system, not the least problem being the prejudice and discrimination leveled at Hispanics. Barrier theory predicts that when such incongruities diminish over time, utilization rates increase; or that in those areas where such incongruities are weak or nonexistent, utilization rates are comparatively higher.

Relevant to the first prediction is the work of Bloom[114] who found that Hispanics in Pueblo, Colorado, went from being underrepresented in regard to inpatient admissions in 1960 to being overrepresented in such admissions in 1970, a finding which also may reflect higher mental health needs among Mexican Americans. The increase was attributed to an improved image of the mental health system, an increase in Chicano staff, and the increased availability of financial aid programs.

Research by Trevino et al.[115] is relevant to the second prediction deriving from barrier theory. The purpose of the research was to select an area predominantly inhabited by Mexican Americans and with a mental health center in which structural barriers had been minimized. The community mental health center chosen was in Laredo, Texas, and had a bilingual Mexican American staff indigenous to the area and utilized a sliding-fee scale in charging for services, but never refused service because of inability to pay. These features of the community mental health center reduced language, cultural, and social class differences, as well as economic barriers. Because the city of Laredo is predominantly Mexican American, the effect of being a member of a minority group also was reduced. The researchers found that for the majority of the census tracts, Mexican Americans met or exceeded their expected utilization of mental health services as determined by the ethnic composition of each tract. The study's conclusions are instructive: ". . . underrepresentation of Mexican Americans in community mental health centers reflects barriers to utilization rather than lower need for service . . .".[116] Thus, the study supports the predictions stemming from barrier theory. The theory has merit. Now we shall examine some of the barriers to mental health care postulated by the theory.

The Spanish language is the centerpiece of a cultural system which is relevant to the utilization of mental health. Edgerton and Karno[117] found that the language selected by Mexican Americans in interviews, Spanish or English, was the best predictor of their beliefs and perceptions regarding depression, juvenile delinquency, schizophrenia, the inheritance of mental illness, the effectiveness of treatment, and familism. Mexican Americans who took the interview in Spanish were more traditional in their answers than those who took it in Engliah, showing traits usually ascribed to the Mexican culture. The Spanish-language respondents considered depression a more serious problem; were less able to tolerate delinquent behavior and more likely to blame the child for such behavior and recommend more drastic measures for its control; more often considered that mental illness is inherited; more often viewed prayer as an effective mode of treatment; believed that the ill person can best be cured by remaining with his family; and more frequently used the term "nervous condition" or simply "nerves" to describe depression and/or schizophrenia. However, both Spanish and English speaking groups agreed upon the existence and seriousness of the problems and upon the effectiveness of psychiatric and nonpsychiatric sources of treatment.

Along with the Spanish language, a configuration of cultural values attributed to Hispanic culture has emerged as relevant to the utilization of mental health facilities. In this regard, the main values mentioned in the literature are: *confianza,* the value of trust,[118] *personalismo,* trust in the immediate person, not the secondary institution;[119] *respeto,* the value of respect intrinsically owed to another person;[120] *verguenza* and *orgullo,* the sense of shame and the value of pride;[121] and *machismo,* the pride in manliness and its associated attributes.[122] Other values are also a part of this configuration, such as familism, fatalism, and orientation toward the present. The literature on utilization treats such values largely as descriptive, ethnographic categories to explain some portion of the variance in Hispanic underutilization of mental health facilities. The underlying argument, however, is seldom made explicit: that such values arise from and reinforce the interpersonal matrix of a primary group society based upon face-to-face intimate relationships. Hispanics adhering to such values, therefore, avoid or experience discomfort in their contacts with impersonal, secondary, bureaucratic organizations such as mental health service agencies. Hence, they underutilize the services of these agencies. Presented in its simplest terms, this argument predicts underutilization or dimished contact with *all* bureaucratic services, not just mental health agencies. Plausible as the argument is because of its commendable use of elements in the ethnic culture, no single piece of research has sought to test directly, and with appropriate controls, the relationship between varying degrees of adherence to this configuration of Hispanic values and rates of utilization of mental health facilities. Were such research to be conducted in the context of the ethnic community's social organization, light would be shed on the important issue of how and when language and values — the two cornerstones of acculturation — affect the process leading to contacts with mental health facilities.

This process is initiated when a person experiencing psychological problems and others in his or her immediate environment perceive the need for help. One would expect that such perceptions, as well as the interpretations which inevitably are made of them, are subject to cultural variability or to differences stemming from levels of acculturation. The findings on this issue, however, are mixed. Some studies find little difference between the ways Anglos and Mexican Americans perceive mental illness,[123] whereas other studies indicate or suggest such differences.[124] Even though Edgerton and Karno[125] see few differences between the two cultures on this point, they still argue that English-speaking Mexican Americans show a higher level of acculturation and thus perceive mental illness in ways more similar to Anglos, while Mexican Americans who speak Spanish regularly had an opposing view. The latter group, for instance, was more likely than the former to believe that mental illness is inherited, with this belief being more characteristic among Mexicans than among Anglos.

Rogler and Hollingshead[126] analyzed the interpretations that Puerto Ricans who had been diagnosed as schizophrenic gave to their illness in a study conducted in the slums and public housing developments of San Juan. The persons diagnosed as schizophrenic viewed their illness as resulting from their being overwhelmed by a variety of symptoms, some of which appear sporadically, and others which disappear only to be replaced by equally tormenting ones. Life problems, social tensions, and conflict were the most common explanations adduced for the illness, while rest and tranquility were desired to allay their overwhelming anxiety and fatigue. In interpreting their own symptoms the schizophrenic persons drew from the folk knowledge of their own Puerto Rican culture. Such interpretations, it would seem, are relevant both to what the afflicted person would be likely to do in seeking help, and to the treatment given to the person by others in the immediate environment. From the foregoing, one would infer that if the emotional disorder is seen as social instead of genetic in origin, greater optimism would attend the help-seeking effort. However, if it is classified as mental illness only when it reaches its most severe forms, treatment will be delayed.[127] There is some evidence that Mexican Americans tend to delay treatment until the illness becomes severe,[128] and that illness is viewed as a manifestation of weakness of character, and the need for treatment, as a disgraceful loss of pride.[129]

Hispanic folk cultures, in fact, have concepts which parallel some of the labels in the vocabulary of mental health practitioners. In the study previously cited, Rogler and Hollingshead[130] examined Puerto Rican cultural conceptions of the role of the *loco* or crazy person. The role of the *loco* is a sharply defined stigma: to become crazy is to lose all socially valued attributes. *Locos* are seen to behave in ways that are antithetical to the society's value system. The deviant behavior of the *loco,* therefore, is viewed in a moral context, thus causing the person to attempt to suppress or avoid divulging his or her symptoms. Unable to do so, the schizophrenic person is classified as crazy and, when punished for being a norm-breaker, he or she withdraws from customary social contacts. The study's data demonstrate that culturally defined labels of deviance associated with mental illness have a pronounced impact upon the afflicted person's help-seeking efforts, the treatment he or she receives in customary relations, and the deeply rooted reluctance to go to a psychiatric hospital which evokes the stigma of *loco.*

In addition to cultural and perceptual differences, there is the possibility that socioeconomic differences between patient and therapist will result in underutilization on the part of Hispanics. The lack of rapport between middle-class therapists and lower-class patients is mentioned frequently,[131] as is the general difficulty of middle-class therapists in working with the poor[132] and with the "non-Yavis" people (patients who are not youthful, attractive, verbal, intelligent, and successful) in general.[133] Since the values of patients can affect utilization of services, so the values of therapists can affect the availability of those services.[134] It is the middle-class character and values of the entire mental health movement that one study sees as one of three major barriers to proper mental health utilization on the part of the poor (the others being fear of institutionalization and attitudes toward mental illness).[135] Here, the authors agree that the literature is replete with middle-class values and orientations toward work, problem-solving, adjustment, conformity, and similar questions. When we consider that blacks have higher rates of utilization than Hispanics, the caution of one study that culture, class, and language interact to cause low Hispanic utilization appears to be well taken.[136] The search for explanations for such complicated interactions should not lead to the neglect of more simple explanations, such as geographic inaccessibility.

Mental health clinics are often located at schools of medicine or universities outside the *barrio*.[137] Even this explanation becomes more complicated in the light of survey reports which show that Mexican Americans aware of nearby clinic locations still have low rates of utilization.[138] Perhaps this is linked to the alleged lack of attention personnel in mental health facilities give to the characteristics of their patients,[139] or to blatant racism in patient selection and treatment.[140]

In sum, barrier theory focuses upon the incongruities and tensions between the collective attributes of Hispanics as actual or potential mental health clients, and the procedures and characteristics of the mental health agency system. Accordingly, explanations for underutilization have been sought in cultural (language and values), perceptual, and social class factors.

At an aggregate or overall level, research relevant to the second phase must include at least four components: (1) epidemiological data on the prevalence and incidence of psychological distress in the Hispanic population designated for research; (2) measures of the degree to which the Hispanic respondents are integrated into the indigenous social organizations serving as alternate mental health resources; (3) measures of the Hispanic respondents' degree of acculturation and of the organizational features of the available mental health service facilities, as indicators of the barriers which impede access to such facilities; and (4) Hispanic utilization rates in the available mental health facilities. The reason for including these four components in a utilization study relevant to the second phase of the framework is that the first three components — the need factor, alternative resources, and the degree of acculturation and agency characteristics — are the major areas upon which the literature converges to explain utilization. If research does not examine the first three components in order to understand the fourth — utilization, the results will inevitably be ambiguous. For example, underutilization in a logical sense could be due to a low need, the existence of strong alternative sources, and the absence of barriers. Or, underutilization could be characterized by a high need, weak alternative resources, and formidable barriers. It is only by viewing the interaction of these three factors through comprehensively organized research that we can begin to narrow the margin of ambiguity.

These are the main features of the research problems relevant to the second phase of the framework seen at the aggregate or general level. As we descend from this level of abstraction to an individual level, we can now see with greater clarity that the emphasis placed upon the time factor in the overarching five-phase model must be projected onto the second phase by conceiving of help-seeking behavior as an attempt over time to cope with psychological distress. However, practically all of the research literature discussed here reveals a surprisingly consistent neglect of the time dimension in the human effort to cope with a mental health problem. It is surprising because the effort to cope, the indicated target of research, is clearly and unmistakably a social process bound by time; yet time plays virtually no role in the research. It is as if the Hispanics' help-seeking efforts had been abstracted out of history and put in a timeless world. The findings of research based upon cross-sectional studies do not capture the time factor. Thus we do not believe there is any possibility of reconciling differences in the findings of the literature reported here or of attaining consistency in the findings of future research unless the research topic is framed as a temporal process.

Let us develop our argument further. We propose that the concept of pathways to the mental health service system is useful because it calls attention to successive contacts from one indigenous social organization to the next or to several at the same time before or while the agency system is contacted. For example, the pathway could be from nuclear to extended family members, intimate friends, folk healers, and then the local community mental health center. The properties of the pathway vary in number, order, and variety of organizations contacted, and in its own duration.

What follows from this proposal is the need to frame research in the clinical services framework's second phase according to the objective and tangible efforts made over time by Hispanics to cope with mental distress. We do not mean to rule out the use of hypothetical questions addressed at Hispanic respondents as to what they would do if certain mental illness symptoms were to be experienced. But hypothetical questions are limited in their use: they bear an unknown and uncertain relationship to what actually does occur, and they cannot be used as proxies. Rather, we need research which delineates pathways concretely in the actual efforts Hispanics make to cope with mental distress. The research could be oriented retrospectively by focusing upon clients forming their first contacts with mental health agencies, or prospectively by identifying the first experience of mental distress and then tracing the coping effort. How the research is in fact oriented will depend upon the specific circumstances.

How does barrier theory fit the approach being proposed? Simply put, barrier theory provides hypotheses which attempt to explain how the help-seeking effort described by the pathway — or by the sequential use of alternative resources, which is the pathway's equivalent — is either suppressed or expedited in moving toward contact with the mental health agency system. Let us provide a specific illustration from *Trapped: Families and Schizophrenia*[141] of how the perception of mental health distress — which, as we have seen, is treated in the literature as a barrier among Hispanics creating underutilization — influences the help-seeking pathway. Mrs. Badillo, a 37-year old woman, began suddenly to have violent fits and seizures in which she would collapse on the floor, her limbs trembling, as she gasped for breath and moaned in a loud, sorrowful voice. Her symptoms conform to what has been described as the Puerto Rican syndrome, an *ataque*.[142] After a long mental health evaluation, a psychiatrist on the research team, not part of the island's service agency system, diagnosed her problem as that of hysterical hyperkinetic seizures. Mrs. Badillo, however, did not take her problem to a professional mental health worker. First, she turned to her husband and then to her neighbors, all of whom advised her that the problem had a spiritual cause. Second, she went to a spiritualist for consulation.

> Yes, I want to consult a spiritualist to see what the attacks meant. The medium told me that there was a young man who was in love with me. The mother-in-law of this young man bewitched me through an evil spirit. This evil spirit takes me over in a violent way.
>
> Do I believe the medium? Of course I do! She described many events in my life that were true. When I see the mother-in-law of this young man I get an attack. This proves that the medium is right.[143]

Since the spiritualist's interpretation of the problem satisfied Mrs. Badillo, she sought no help from persons outside the indigenous organizations. In this case, the pathway was comparatively simple and short, from husband to neighbors and then to the spiritualist, all of whom framed the problem according to spiritualist ideology. The way the problem is perceived — which is one of the variables in barrier theory — conditions the pathway.

Let us pursue the illustration a step further. Had Mrs. Badillo's problem been perceived to have material cause in addition to a spiritual cause, she probably would have consulted with both a medium and a professional mental health practitioner, or one person commanding both sets of skills, as the following quote would suggest. The prevailing view of the *Trapped* respondents regarding the division of labor between spiritualist and psychiatrist (or mental health practitioner) was clearly stated by one person.

> Mediums understand things that the doctor-psychiatrist does not; that is, if the doctor is not a spiritualist. If psychiatrists were to know about spiritual matters they would be doctors in the broadest sense of the word. When the doctor does not know about spiritual matters, he should consult with a spiritualist, and in this way they could come to an agreement. Spiritualists would

treat the spiritual part of the problem and thereby rid the individual of possible evil spirits. Psychiatrists could treat the nervous system, if this were affected. There would be much success then.[144]

The opinion quoted above allows us to make the point that awareness and acceptability of the professional facilities are factors that bear an immediate relevance to the pathway described. These components, together with accessibility and availability, are suggested by the National Institute of Mental Health for assessing the utilization of community mental health centers.[145] Thus, the example of Mrs. Badillo indicates an awareness of professional mental health services, which, however, were not considered acceptable because the problem was not perceived as having its origins in the nervous system. Her perception of the problem as a spiritual one detaches her from the professional system because she is rooted in the indigenous system. Such perceptions, influential in relation to the pathway, are drawn from culturally based ideologies of mental health. The perception of the mental health problem acted as a barrier toward the utilization of the professional system.

Freidson's typology[146] of lay referral systems sheds light on the issues being discussed. What Freidson conceives as a lay referral system is what we have been describing as the pathway through primary social organizations. Thus, lay referral systems should be understood as consisting not only of persons and groups providing referrals, although this component is included, but also as an interpersonal system that diagnoses and provides treatment. His typology is based upon the combination of two elements: (1) the congruence or incongruence between the lay and professional culture according to elements we have previously described, such as language, values, and the perceptions of illness and of appropriate treatments; and (2) the structure of the lay referral system which may be loose and truncated or cohesive and extended. If the structure is loose and truncated, the persons are left on their own in the consultation process or they consult only with members of their immediate families. If it is cohesive and extended it reinforces the beliefs and values of the people. The combination of the elements yields four types of lay referral systems. For our purposes the most important type is the one which combines an incongruity between lay referral culture and professional medical culture, on the one hand, and a lay referral structure which is extended and cohesive, on the other hand. In this type, the help-seeking effort occurs as a sequence of steps through the extended and cohesive lay referral system (the indigenous social organizations), before contact is made with the professional system. Delays in contacting the professional system or the avoidance of the system are due to the availability of an extended and cohesive group of help givers, and to the fact that membership in such a group reinforces the cultural incompatibility between the lay and professional system. This conception of help-seeking as a social process highlights the temporal dimension we already have emphasized.

The Hispanics' efforts to cope with psychological problems unmistakably fit this type of lay referral system as is evident in the literature we have reviewed, and in other literature as well.[147] Not only do they fit in a descriptive sense, but the predictions which derive from this type of lay referral system conform to the Hispanics' low utilization rates of mental health services. The studies previously discussed,[148] which have shown that the use of bilingual, bicultural staff and of paraprofessionals indigenous to the ethnic community reduces barriers and increases utilization, can be understood in the context of Freidson's general typology of lay referral systems: When the lay referral systems (or the indigenous social organizations) are socially or structurally intertwined with the mental health system and the cultural differences between the two are thus reduced, utilization rates among Hispanics increase. The professional system reaches out to the cohesive and extended lay referral system to increase its accessibility and to assimilate elements of indigenous or lay culture in the interest of attracting persons to use its services.

Two studies currently underway at the Hispanic Research Center attempt to integrate epidemiological data on the prevalence of psychological distress in the Hispanic population, alternative resource theory and barrier theory — the major areas upon which the literature converges to explain utilization — into a comprehensive examination of Hispanic utilization of mental health services. The first study aims to discover the extent of actual utilization of a broad spectrum of services among black, Hispanic, and white residents of an area in the south-central Bronx in New York City.[149] To obtain a generalized measure of psychological distress, the study administered to respondents a 27-point Demoralization Scale[150] which measures eight clusters of symptoms: dread, self-esteem, hopelessness-helplessness, anxiety, confused thinking, sadness, psychophysiological symptoms, and poor physical health. Hispanics, it was found, have the highest number of symptomatic responses in all but one symptom cluster — poor self-esteem, where Hispanics and blacks have equal scores. Overall, Hispanics have a mean symptomatic score significantly higher than blacks or whites. The majority of demoralized individuals — those who had nine or more symptoms (the average number of symptoms for respondents who indicated in a separate question that they had had an emotional problem in the past twelve months) — did not use mental health services. Overall, only 20 percent of demoralized individuals report receiving as many mental health services as they needed, and 10 percent received some services but fewer than they reported needed. One-fifth of demoralized respondents acknowledge having emotional problems but needing no services, while half report no emotional problems, and therefore do not seek mental health services. Thus, a significant number of persons in the area are not receiving needed mental health services.

Based on the preliminary findings of this study, the Hispanic Research

Center has developed a direct service intervention project called COPA (Community Organization and Patient Access). This study attempts to identify the barriers which keep the Hispanic chronically mentally ill from utilizing mental health services; implement culturally sensitive intervention approaches to overcome these barriers; and evaluate the effectiveness of these interventions under actual service conditions. While the data used to design interventions in the project inform both alternative resources and barrier theories, the study focuses on the factor most amenable to change within a short period of time, namely, institutional barriers. This study is one in which research leads to planned intervention to successively reduce barriers and to the implementation of interventions whose impact on utilization, is, in turn, monitored by research.

In sum, alternative resource theory and barrier theory can be integrated to provide a more dynamic and comprehensive framework for research focusing upon the clinical services framework's second phase. The use of such a framework should capture more accurately and extensively the Hispanic experience of mental health service utilization, and thus improve mental health policy and practice affecting the Hispanic community.

# *Phase 3:*
# EVALUATION OF MENTAL HEALTH

Phase 3 involves the mental health assessment of Hispanic clients who have reached a treatment setting. Here we shall briefly consider the diagnostic process and discuss selected surrounding issues, problems, and possible diagnostic alternatives.

A client's early contacts with a mental health agency are likely to be diagnostic in nature, whether the assessment performed is formal or informal, brief or extensive. The procedure might include a mental status examination, an interview in which the client's present contact with reality and personal orientation are assessed. Psychological tests might be administered such as an individual intelligence test (e.g., WAIS-R, WISC-R, Stanford-Binet), projective techniques (e.g., Rorschach, thematic apperception test, drawings) in which a client projects aspects of his or her personality onto ambiguous stimuli, a psychometric paper and pencil personality test (e.g., MMPI), or a neurological screening device (e.g., Bender). A social history is taken to place test and interview data in con'ext. At the end of this process, a diagnosis is assigned, a disposition made, and a treatment plan developed.

The question of whether the instruments used in assessment and even the interview process itself are culturally biased has been hotly debated, but the presence of differences between ethnic groups on tasks and qualities attributable to the process·of assessment is indisputable. These differences suggest that something other than the qualities whch the tests are designed to measure is at issue.

Differences have been reported in diverse comparisons between members of Hispanic and other ethnic groups. Durrett and Kim[151] found that Mexican American preschool children were less behaviorally mature than their Anglo counterparts; Haberman's field studies[152] indicate that Puerto Ricans consistently tend to report more psychiatric symptoms than other groups; Kagan and Romero[153] found that non-adaptive, assertive behavior was more prominent among Anglo than Mexican American children. LeVine and Padilla[154] list a number of personality tests on which Hispanics' performance differed from that of other ethnic groups. They concluded that projective tests tap personality factors as they vary with cultural and social milieu, and that cultural ideology and acculturation level may affect choices made on objective personality measures.

Although Korchin[155] discusses alternatives, assessment typically involves the implicit or explicit comparisons of the behavior or response of the examinee with that of other people. For example, on intelligence and psychometric personality tests, an individual's performance is compared with group norms. Hence, a Hispanic client may appear at the lower end of the non-minority group norms, yet be within or close to the average range for his or her own ethnic group. The impact of such misinterpretation of test performance on people's lives can be dramatic. As Reschley, Mercer, Garcia and McClelland[156] show, a disproportionate number of minority children are overclassified as mentally retarded and emotionally disturbed.

On more open-ended tasks, such as interviews or projective tests, clinicians may make use of group norms and/or make a qualitative comparison of an individual's performance with a generalized view of a healthy person. In any case, the more performance diverges from the clinician's view of normal, the more noteworthy it becomes. Hence, the question of what frame of reference is being used is of the utmost importance for minority group clients, since norms have meaning only if they are appropriate for the individual being considered. Not surprisingly, a prominent theme in the literature of minority assessment is the need to develop appropriate norms.

Cole's discussion of bias in testing[157] is based on the premise that questions of bias are questions of validity — whether the tests accurately measure what they purport to measure. Based on her review, she concluded that differential predictive validity and bias in internal test structure have not been established for the tests and groups studied. It is noteworthy that her discussion revolves around a comparison of black and white groups, and that LeVine and Padilla's review points to differences in obtained test results from blacks and Hispanics. However, Cole's distinction between the issues of validity and whether certain tests should be used, even if valid, is well taken. She points out that consideration of the possibility of test bias arose from concern with equitable treatment of special groups within our pluralistic society, and that these broader issues of social policy and implementation cannot be reduced to a matter of test bias. One of the major questions which she raises is how we should deal socially and educationally with people for whom English is not a first language.

The flagrant difficulties involved in testing a non-English-speaking client cannot be denied. When a Hispanic client who speaks no English is being assessed by an English-speaking diagnostician, an interpreter's services are needed. As Marcos[158] pointed out, any available person (a family member or a bystander) may be pressed into service. Interpreter-related distortions may give rise to important misconceptions about the patient's mental health status. These distortions are most frequently associated with defective linguistic and/or translation skills of the interpreter; the interpreter's lack of psychiatric knowledge; and the interpreter's self-imposed role and attitude toward either patient or the clinician. In a poignant article, Sabin[159] discussed two case histories of Spanish-speaking clients who had been evaluated and treated by English-speaking clinicians by use of translation. Sabin suggests that these patients' emotional problems were selectively underestimated and their anxiety inadequately translated. When the client appears able to participate in an assessment process conducted in English, another set of problems is posed. In a compelling study, Marcos et al.[160] discovered that interviews conducted in the client's non-preferred language yield a clinical judgment of greater pathology.

Important as the issue of language is, it is surrounded by the still larger issue of biculturalism. Mercer[161] provides a discussion of the impact of biculturalism on the assessment of Hispanic clients. One of her major conclusions is that the IQ tests used by psychologists to measure, among other things, the extent to which an individual's background is similar to that of modal American society. This conclusion could be investigated with respect to other types of tests as well.

A number of alternatives to the system of assessment as it now exists have been proposed. Mercer[162] discusses a number of approaches that aim to be neither racially nor culturally discriminatory. She considers that it is virtually impossible to have culture-free tests since all learning takes place in a sociocultural context. Alternatives include modification of existing tests (translating, rewriting, etc.) and construction of culture-specific tests developed for each sociocultural group.[163] Mercer also points out that such tests face the same problem of being tied to a single ethnic group, albeit in reverse of the Anglo-centric test currently in use. Mercer's own alternative is a System of Multicultural Pluralistic Assessment (SOMPA)[164] designed to assess the current level of functioning and the potential of low-SES children from Anglo, Chicano, and black cultural backgrounds. She discusses how children can be considered in comparison to both standardized norms for tests and those developed for the sociocultural group to which the individual belongs. Although she has focused on assessment of intelligence, these principles could also be investigated in relation to personality assessment.

Research on the assessment of Hispanic clients points to the many topics which warrant further exploration. Representative topics will be mentioned briefly. LeVine and Padilla's review[165] of the are of self-disclosure among Hispanics, consistently at a lower level than that for Anglos, has important implications for the diagnostic process, since clinicians may find it difficult to obtain information of a personal nature. Some of the studies are qualitative and descriptive in nature. Rogler and Hollingshead[166] and Grace[167] present a portrayal of an *ataque nervioso* which may occur when the Hispanic individual is confronted with an overwhelming catastrophe. If the *ataque* is separated from its cultural context, major pathology could be inferred from the screaming, falling, lack of communication, and agitated motor movement evidenced by such individuals. The subject of stereotyping has also received considerable attention among both the general population[168] and clinicians.[169] These considerations suggest that the client's ethnic group affects clinical judgment about that client.

In their study of Hispanics, blacks, and whites in a psychiatric hospital in the South Bronx, Baskin et al.[170] also found a relationship between the patient's ethnicity and psychiatric diagnosis. Hispanic psychiatric patients were more frequently diagnosed as having depressive/affective disorders, transient situational disturbances, and non-psychotic disorders in comparison to blacks and whites. In another study, the Baskin group[171] explored diagnostic differences between men and women of the above three ethnic groups. The most prevalent diagnoses among the total group of Hispanics were non-psychotic disorders, transient situational disturbances, alcoholism, depressive/affective disorders, and schizophrenia. Proportions differed by sex within the ethnic group. For instance, more men carried the diagnosis of alcoholism than women; while more women than men were diagnosed as having non-psychotic disorders. The evaluation of mental health, thus, is the outcome of a complicated process in which interview language and interviewer ethnicity play an important role.

As we have seen, there is great interest in the impact of bilingualism and biculturalism on psychiatric diagnosis. As far back as the 1930's, Velikovsky[172] questioned whether a newly acquired language could assess the unconscious, and later Buxbaum[173] expressed a related concern over the effect of a second language on the formation of ego and superego. Similarly, subsequent reports have focused on the role of language in facilitating and disrupting the therapeutic process,[174] while others have dealt with linguistically differential responses to drugs,[175] electroconvulsive therapy,[176] and aphasia.[177]

Early on, psychiatric epidemiological studies revealed that the incidence of psychotic diagnoses among ethnic minority populations is significantly higher compared to non-minority populations, particularly for Hispanics.[178] Gross, Knatterud, and Donner,[179] for example, reported that ethnic minority patients were more likely to be diagnosed as schizophrenic and then treated in a psychiatric emergency room than non-minority patients who, in turn, tended to be more often diagnosed as neurotic and subsequently referred to outpatient psychiatric service. Similar trends have been reported even more recently in surveys of black and Hispanic patients, as contrasted with white patients, at large community mental health centers and psychiatric hospitals.[180]

One interpretation of these statistics in the Hispanic population suggests that either features inherent to the Hispanic culture or stress induced by migration to the United States may predispose individuals toward psychological disorder.[181] Alternately, others have argued that clinical judgments of psychopathology with Hispanic patients reflect interviewer bias, particularly since psychiatric personnel are principally white, middle-class, and English-speaking. This viewpoint is based upon the notion that as sociocultural distance between clinician and patient increases, diagnoses become less accurate.[182] In this regard, Karno[183] concluded that unacculturated Hispanics who encounter traditional white clinicians react with relative passivity, deference, and inhibited silence, thus leading clinicians to misinterpret the behavior expressed in psychiatric interviews. Further, Karno speculated that, since the psychiatric "historical" interview derives from the medical model, an exclusionary bias operates upon sociocultural factors which may be crucial to both diagnosis and treatment. Effects of such bias have been noted by Thomas,[184] among others, who linked clinicians' culturally stereotypical attitudes to the provocation of irrational behavior in the patient, not as a result of underlying pathology, but as a result of the clinician's attitude or behavior. Still other evidence by Carkhuff and Pierce[185] suggests that ethnic similarity between patient and clinician is associated with more profound self-exploration in psychiatric interviews, in comparison to ethnically disparate patient-clinician dyads.

Thus, much of the literature on the psychiatric evaluation of Hispanics highlights the ubiquity of misdiagnosis by non-Hispanic clinicians, presumably as a consequence of sociocultural barriers emerging in psychiatric interviews. Foremost among such barriers appears to be the interaction of bilingualism and biculturalism.[186] Edgerton and Karno[187] reported that English-dominant Hispanics were indistinguishable from non-Hispanics in responding to psychiatric vignettes, yet Spanish-dominant Hispanics tended to express themes of fatalism, familism, attachment to religious values, and patriarchal authoritarianism, which are cultural characteristics often misinterpreted as pathological by non-Hispanic clinicians. The importance of clinician awareness of bilingualism, especially age of second language acquisition, has been stressed by Peck[188] who commented that, first, English acquisition in adulthood often leads to speech distortion which in turn is misinterpreted due to clinicians' stereotypical attitudes toward bilinguals and, second, bilinguals frequently experience a loss in second language fluency under stressful conditions, which is likely to be the case in a psychiatric interview.

Acknowledging that bilingualism and language of interview are principal factors impugning accurate psychiatric diagnosis, the questions arise: In which language, English or Spanish, do bilingual Hispanics express greater psychopathology? What is the true nature and degree of pathology? Unfortunately, literature focusing on the first question is equivocal, while the second question has not been addressed experimentally.

Based upon a small sample of clinical case histories, Del Castillo[189] related from personal experience that Hispanic psychiatric patients appeared highly psychotic when interviewed in Spanish, but much less so when interviewed in English. From this evidence, Del Castillo reasoned that psychotic processes are ideationally represented in the native language, but speaking a less familiar second language compels the patient to confront

**41**

reality.

Contrary to Del Castillo's clinical observations, a series of experimental studies by Marcos and others[190] provides evidence that English-speaking clinicians interpret greater pathology during English interviews than Spanish-speaking clinicians during Spanish interviews. Focusing on the dynamics of the interview situation, Price and Cuellar[191] and Vazquez[192] criticized the Marcos studies, independently recognizing significant sources of confounding in Marcos' experimental design.

Although Marcos carefully blinded his clinicians to the purpose of the study and minimized intrusive behavior on their part, language of interview and ethnicity of clinical diagnosticians were confounded. Interestingly enough, when such confounding was eliminated, with bilingual Hispanic clinicians evaluating both English and Spanish interviews, results contradicted Marcos' findings and corroborated Del Castillo's observations of greater psychopathology expressed in Spanish.

Reacting to the confusion in the literature, Vazquez stressed the tentativeness of Del Castillo's case-study approach, and the inconclusiveness of Marcos' studies, inasmuch as his findings may be a function of interview language or sociocultural bias on the part of clinicians, or both. Moreover, Vazquez proceeded to discover a number of flaws in Price and Cuellar's attempted replication.

First, one source of discrepancy between studies was that Marcos studied recent admissions to a large, urban psychiatric hospital, whereas Price and Cuellar studied relatively chronic, hospitalized patients — with much more experience in a psychiatric setting — who were treated in a culturally sensitive milieu. As Vazquez remarked, inexperienced patients may indeed express more pathology in English, but prior interview experience may promote greater disclosure and hence more pathology in Spanish. Second, given that bilingual clinicians evaluated both Spanish and English interviews, thus avoiding confounding of clinician ethnicity and language of interview, paradoxically this rendered tacit experimental blinding of clinicians unlikely. Third, Marcos eliminated possible intrusion of interviewer behavior on patient behavior through a standardized audiotaped interview, while Price and Cuellar, on the other hand, attempted to preserve the ecological validity of the psychiatric interview by employing *in vivo* interviewers.

Clearly, the interplay of sociocultural and linguistic factors in the dynamics of the psychiatric interviews need to be experimentally isolated and disentangled in future research efforts. It is only by this means that an understanding can be achieved of the mode of language expression representative of the true nature and degree of psychopathology experienced by bilingual Hispanic patients.

Another issue of long-standing debate in the field of psychological assessment is the cultural appropriateness of using with minorities instruments that have been standardized primarily on white and middle-class groups. While some attempts have been made to develop culturally sensitive intelligence and personality tests for blacks[193] as well as for Hispanics,[194] unfortunately, these instruments have not withstood psychometric evaluation.[195] With respect to projective personality tests, minority children, as we have seen, have been evaluated as less verbal, less emotionally responsive, and more psychopathological than their non-minority counterparts.[196] Challenging these findings, several investigators have argued that urban minority children are not inherently deficient, inasmuch as traditional standardized tests fail to accurately measure the intellectual, cognitive, personality, and affective functioning of minority children.[197]

An early attempt to develop a culturally relevant projective test was made by Thompson,[198] who changed the white characters of Murray's TAT[199] into black characters, based upon the notion that the closer test stimuli resemble the examiner, the more the examinee identifies with the stimuli, hence the greater likelihood of test stimuli eliciting meaningful responses.[200] Preliminary findings indicated that black college students showed an increase in verbal productivity in response to the black TAT; however, subsequent studies failed to replicate these results.[201] Murstein[202] later attributed the apparent lack of validity of the black TAT to the fact that (1) blacks are not a socioeconomically homogeneous group; (2) a high degree of similarity between the test stimuli and the testee tends to increase ego defensiveness; and (3) simple verbal productivity seems to be an inadequate criterion of test validity. However, other investigators[203] have suggested that the black TAT lacked validity for blacks because (1) only TAT characters were altered, while original TAT backgrounds and themes were retained; (2) college students were not representative of the general ·black population; and (3) the instrument was introduced at a time when prejudice against blacks was higher than today.

Notwithstanding the early discouraging findings with regard to the black TAT, Cowan and Goldberg[204] studied the effects of race and sex of TAT characters on achievement motivation of black males and females using original TAT characters with altered racial characteristics. Cowan and Goldberg reported that black characters stimulated higher verbal productivity and achievement motivation than white characters. Similarly, Bailey and Green[205] compared Murray's TAT, Thompson's TAT, and an experimental TAT developed to reflect black features in a more culturally congruent manner than previous attempts. These investigators found that black males clearly discriminated the black figures of the experimental TAT, characters were judged more like "people in general," and verbal productivity was enhanced. Thus, Bailey and Green concluded that projective test stimuli culturally and racially congruent with the examinee were valuable in enhancing the meaningfulness of the response.

In the light of the compelling need for a culturally sensitive projective test for Hispanics, the Hispanic Research Center is developing Costantino's TEMAS (Tell-Me-A-Story) thematic apperception test consisting of pictures depicting interactions among urban ethnic minority figures, minority cultural

43

themes and symbols, and urban backgrounds.[206] The instrument was developed from the notion that projective test stimuli ought to be sensitive to the cultural background of the examinee in order to elicit sufficient verbal productivity and meaningful response. The pictures were developed by a clinical psychologist in collaboration with a professional artist to accurately represent the ethnic features of Hispanics in realistic urban settings. The stimuli depict situations involving underlying psychological conflict (e.g., complying with a parental errand vs. playing with peers) in order to elicit responses reflective of adaptiveness of personality functioning. TEMAS stimuli are presented in full color to further enhance the realism of the situations depicted in the pictures. Each TEMAS picture was developed to "pull" particular personality functions, such as delay of gratification, achievement motivation, self-concept of competence, or anxiety and withdrawal. The psychometric value of TEMAS with respect to traditional projective tests such as TAT, CAT, Rorschach, Draw-A-Person, and House-Tree-Person rests on the following factors: (1) the use of chromatic, nonambiguous and familiar stimuli to elicit diagnostically meaningful stories; (2) the representation of both negative and positive polarities of affects, cognitions, intrapersonal functioning and interpersonal relationships; (3) the assessment of the interaction between affective, cognitive, intrapersonal and interpersonal factors focusing on both motivational and overt personality function levels; and (4) the use of an objective scoring system in analyzing TEMAS stories, which will yield both normative data and clinical-intuitive understanding of personality and degree of psychopathology.

In one study, Costantino, Malgady and Vazquez[207] compared Hispanic, black, and white children's verbal fluency on the TAT and TEMAS. An urban sample of 72 Hispanic, 41 black, and 43 white children (grades K-6) were administered a minority TEMAS, a parallel TEMAS depicting non-minority characters, and the TAT. Results indicated that females were more verbally fluent on the TEMAS than the TAT; and whites evidenced no significant differences in verbal fluency. The increased verbal fluency of minority children on TEMAS seems to be associated primarily with such factors as cultural themes, urban backgrounds, contemporary characters, reduced ambiguity, and chromatic stimuli; and only secondarily associated with the minority characters depicted in TEMAS pictures.

In sum, research in the third phase of the conceptual framework focuses on the currently prominent issue of traditional assessment procedures for psychodiagnosis and evaluation, and on the effects of bilingualism, language of the psychiatric interview, and ethnicity of the examiner on psychodiagnosis.

## *Phase 4:*
# THERAPEUTIC MODALITIES

The fourth phase of the HRC's conceptual framework focuses upon the development and evaluation of culturally sensitive therapeutic modalities for use with Hispanic clients. We shall briefly discuss major issues in this phase of research, such as assignment to treatment, type and duration of treatment, therapy process and outcome.

The first major issue in this phase of the conceptual framework, simply put, is what sort of patient gets assigned to which type of treatment. Since the question of how Hispanic clients are assigned to treatment has received little direct attention, the body of research concerning low-income clients is worthy of consideration. There is ample documentation showing that as a group, Hispanics are economically disadvantaged compared to non-Hispanics.[208] It is, therefore, appropriate to raise the question of whether the more general findings about treatment assignment of low-income clients are relevant to Hispanic clients. The relationship between social class and obtained therapeutic treatment is striking. Lower class clients are less likely to receive clinical services, and those who are treated receive services considered less prestigious. This pattern was described in the now classic work by Hollingshead and Redlich,[209] and upheld in the follow-up study by Myers and Bean.[210] Recent reviews by Lorion, Parloff, and Sue reveal that little has changed over the past four decades.[211]

In a much cited discussion, Schofield[212] described therapists' preference for the client who is YAVIS, or young, attractive, verbal, intelligent, and successful, as opposed to the HOUND patient described by Goldstein and Simonson[213] as "homely, old, unattractive, nonverbal and dumb." Adams and McDonald[214] described the ways in which poor people are discouraged from seeking psychotherapy and referred to less prestigious services. Clearly, the question of whether traditional therapies have been made available to lower class clients and/or are responsive to their needs is complex and problematical.

In his appraisal of the development of psychotherapy during the past forty years, Garfield[215] pointed to the increasing number of therapies which are currently practiced. Teichner, Cadden and Berry[216] discuss the need to adapt traditional therapeutic frameworks when working with Puerto Rican clients. Green et al.[217] make the same point in regard to Mexican children. However, the view of these and other authors is that certain therapeutic modalities are either intrinsically in keeping with Hispanic values or readily lend themselves to adaptation. Family therapy has been identified as an appropriate treatment approach by a number of authors such as Szapocznik, Johnson et al., and Boulette.[218] Fink also discusses how psychodrama,[219] group therapy,[220] and assertiveness training[221] have been used in a culturally appropriate manner. On the other hand, elements of these therapies, such as confrontation, attack, and sex reversal role-playing, are recognized as being unacceptable to many Hispanic clients.

Innovative modalities, that is, those designed with cultural considerations in mind, include Szapocznik's Life Enhancement Therapy,[222] a psychosocial approach designed to enhance the meaningfulness of life for Cuban elders, thereby alleviating depression. Another expressly Hispanic modality is Maldonado-Sierra and Trent's method of group therapy used with Puerto Rican schizophrenics.[223] A three-member therapy team representing significant members of a family provides treatment for a patient group, with attention given to relationships among patients, who play the role of siblings. Ruiz[224] makes the point, however, that not all Hispanic clients have the same need for treatment approaches that are geared toward this group. He proposes a continuum of acculturation from "completely Hispanic" to "completely Anglo." The more acculturated the client, the less the need for approaches specifically attuned to Hispanics.

Whatever the mode of treatment used, the question of whether appointments will be kept and treatment sustained is paramount. Sue et al.[225] found that Chicanos terminated counseling after only one contact at a rate of 50 percent, in sharp contrast to the 30 percent rate for Anglos. Miranda[226] reported that Mexican American women electing to remain in psychotherapy for a minimum of five sessions demonstrated higher levels of both psychological and behavioral acculturation than those women who terminated treatment prematurely. In their review of the types of factors which affect the likelihood of clients' dropping out of treatment, Baekeland and Lundwell[227] identify two factors which apply to Hispanics. Low socioeconomic status clients are more likely to drop out of treatment, a finding which may be applicable to Hispanic clients. Clients who are not able to see or label causal relationships between ideas and feelings pertaining to one's self and behavior are also more likely to drop out. This finding too is relevant to the large proportion of Hispanic clients whose concerns with economic survival preclude contemplations of the more rarified aspects of the human condition. This is in keeping with Maslow's view of personality,[228] which acknowledges that physiological and safety needs must be met before the psychological needs for belonging, with love, esteem, and self-actualization can be realized.

Therapy dropouts are an elusive group for mental health professionals to study. Hence, Acosta's study[229] is a valuable contribution to this area of inquiry. Anglo, black, and Mexican dropouts showed no significant differences in their reasons given for terminating therapy. Reasons provided were negative attitudes toward therapists and perception of therapy as not beneficial. This finding is in keeping with the discussion of Acosta, Evans et at.[230] who consider dropping out a result of unmet role expectations. Even when Hispanic clients are engaged in culturally appropriate, community-based treatment, external factors may work against involvement in long-term treatment. For instance, the duration of Aloyo's therapeutic work[231] with agricultural migrant workers depended not on the evolution of a therapeutic relationship but on the harvest cycle: when a seasonal crop was harvested, the clients moved on and therapy was terminated or suspended. In more traditional settings, one method of attempting to counter the high dropout rate is to provide new clients with an informational introduction to the nature of therapy through role induction.[232] In Acosta's introduction, appropriately titled "Telling It Like It Is," clients are shown a cassette program which prepares them for their role as a client. Other programs also prepare therapists for work with low-income clients.[233]

Engaging Hispanic clients in therapy is only a first step. Though the issue has been incompletely explored, some findings suggest that there are important process variables which must be taken into account when working with Hispanic clients. Sue[234] points out that Hispanics prefer an active therapist, perceive the therapist as an authority, and have been reared to show respect for authority figures by not speaking until spoken to. Acosta and Scheehan[235] found that Mexican American college students were less willing to provide self-disclosing information than their Anglo counterparts though both groups showed some willingness to self-disclose. Cross and Maldonado[236] indicate that Chicanos were reluctant to reveal personal matters to those outside the family.

Process research, concerned with events which transpire within the therapy session in the interaction between the therapist and the client, is also worthy of attention.[237] Sue's review notes Hollingshead and Redlich's findings that lower class patients tend to have less intensive therapeutic relationships.[238] It should also be kept in mind that findings about the effect of process variables in the population at large may operate differently with Hispanic clients. For instance, the true importance of therapist characteristics — genuineness, unconditional positive regard, and empathy — which Rogers[239] proposed as necessary for constructive personality change to occur in the client, has been widely debated.[240] Green[241] discusses the importance Mexican Americans place on positive interpersonal relationships. Whether genuineness, unconditional positive regard, and empathy are the interpersonal qualities likely to facilitate the therapeutic process with Hispanics is worthy of exploration, as is the more general question of whether process considerations, demonstrated in the population at large, generalize to Hispanics.

As with the process considerations, the extent to which general therapy outcome findings are applicable to Hispanics is important. The question of whether or not therapy is more effective than no treatment has been a much debated issue[242] since Eysenck's controversial claim[243] that therapy clients fared no better than those on a waiting list. Over the past decades, his data have been reanalyzed and his claim countered. The consensus of the profession is that therapy is more effective than no treatment, as supported by "tally" type reviews of the literature[244] and more recently by Smith and Glass's meta-analysis[245] of psychotherapeutic outcome studies, in which data from 375 studies were combined, yielding the conclusion that the typical therapy client is better off than 75 percent of untreated controls. It is interesting to juxtapose Lorion's indication[246] that there is no difference by social class in the success of therapeutic outcome with Garfield's observation[247] that there has been a visible decline in the importance of psychoanalytically oriented therapies and long-term therapies in general. The concomitantly greater emphasis on therapies which are briefer and more active may be more likely to provide successful outcomes for lower class and Hispanic clients.

As Paul[248] pointed out, the general question of which psychotherapy is most effective can best be considered in terms of components. What treatment by whom is most effective for this individual with that problem and under which set of circumstances? Introduction of the ethnic group of the client, the therapist, and the surrounding cultural considerations adds a new dimension to these queries. Unfortunately, the studies which address therapy outcome in the Hispanic population are small and incomplete fragments of the entire picture. For instance, Boulette[249] compared the effectiveness of therapeutic listening and behavioral rehearsal on depressed Mexican American women and reported that neither approach was consistently effective. Acosta and Scheehan's finding[250] that Mexican Americans attributed more trustworthiness and skill to a Mexican American therapist when portrayed as a paraprofessional and to an Anglo when portrayed as a professional is noteworthy, given Frank's view[251] that the client's expectation of help from and faith in the therapist are elements common to all types of therapy. The Acosta and Scheehan study serves to underscore the notion that findings about the effect of therapist variables, such as race, perceived expertise, and interaction, uncovered from studies among mainstream Americans, may not generalize to Hispanics.

Though not conducted with Hispanic clients, Heffernon and Bruehl's study[252] is worth considering when addressing the issues of therapist variables, client preferences, and outcome. They found that although black children generally showed a stronger preference for black versus white therapists, one particular white therapist with experience with this clinical population was also strongly favored. Although there are sometimes advantages in matching a client to a therapist of the same ethnic group, this match cannot be considered a panacea for the problems of minority group clients. Muñoz[253] provides a poignant discussion of his own difficulties in treating Hispanic Americans, pointing out that minority group therapists who have recently emerged from poor communities may attribute their clients' problems to socioeconomic conditions even when the problem has a truly intrapsychic basis. Cummings[254] reported that when a group practice of therapists has an appropriate proportion of minority and female therapists, clients' demands for a certain type of therapist tend to disappear. Clearly, the issue is worthy of further consideration.

Barrett, Hampe and Miller,[255] in their discussion of research on childhood psychotherapy, lament the lack of resources directed toward disorders of childhood. Their review considers child psychotherapy research as no match in quantity or quality with the corresponding body of research on adults. The authors were particularly disconcerted by the lack of substantive attempts to grapple with the significant issues related to child psychotherapy. Ethnic minority youngsters tend to experience a disproportionately high incidence of mental disorder relative to their non-minority counterparts in urban settings, and furthermore, low socioeconomic status ethnic youngsters tend to underutilize traditional psychotherapeutic intervention facilities.[256] Moreover, youngsters in this population who attend traditional mental health clinics tend to drop out of psychotherapy early in treatment, thus failing to benefit from the intervention.[257]

The Report to the President's Commission on Mental Health[258] pointed out that a large percentage of American children grow into adulthood with mental disorders which might have been ameliorated through earlier psychotherapeutic intervention. Although an estimated 12 million youngsters under the age of 18 are currently affected by mental disorders only about one million are in psychotherapeutic treatment. Thus, the 92 percent of these youngsters who remain psychologically untreated represent high risks for continued or more severe mental disorders when they reach adulthood.[259] Within this population, two million Hispanic and black youngsters, mostly from low socioeconomic backgrounds, are estimated to have severe mental health problems.[260]

One Hispanic Research Center study has demonstrated that school-age Puerto Rican children frequently experience serious personality disturbances and present higher risks for mental disorders than their white counterparts due to a vast array of economic, educational, and, above all, psychological and bilingual factors.[261] Hispanic youngsters have been found to experience emotional disorientation, feelings of inferiority, and very poor self-esteem.[262] Furthermore, black youngsters experience similar problems, having been found to present more psychopathology than white youngsters.[263] Black youngsters, like bilingual Hispanic youngsters, also are reported to have inferiority feelings, low self-esteem, high trait anxiety, and low school achievement.[264] Thus, there appears to be a compelling need to develop culturally sensitive modalities to remediate the psychological problems of ethnic minority youngsters in need of psychotherapy.

An example of an attempt in this direction is the Unitas Therapeutic Community located in the South Bronx (New York). The Unitas program comprises several hundred primarily black and Hispanic youngsters, ranging in age from 5 to 16. About half of the Unitas participants are referred to the program by parents or teachers as "problem children," usually evidencing severe symptoms of psychopathology such as withdrawal or bizarre behavior. The remainder of Unitas participants attend the program voluntarily, although they may not necessarily manifest maladaptive behaviors indicative of potential mental disorder.

Unitas is founded upon the concept of the family unit as the most important natural institution that can satisfy a child's need for nurturance and discipline. Unitas, therefore, has created a system of symbolic families composed of up to 15 boys and girls, usually living on the same street, but not necessarily from the same biological family. Each symbolic family is headed by one or two older neighborhood teenagers who play the roles of symbolic mothers, fathers, aunts, and uncles. These teenagers receive intensive training in psychological therapy and clinical skills and become the primary caretakers and therapists of the younger children. Thus, Unitas' concept of therapeutic intervention is based upon the creation of a therapeutic community as a form of milieu therapy which stresses the importance of cultivating a positive and mutually helpful environment within the context of the treatment setting. In addition to the therapeutic community, an interpersonal model of psychotherapy is the primary approach used in Unitas to effect its goal of treatment of psychological and psychiatric disorders. This interpersonal model relies on an "extended family circle" as community therapy, as well as on play and family therapy. Unitas' highly active system of sanctions, which rewards valued behavior and the mastery of interpersonal skills while discouraging undesirable conduct, creates external pressure on the participants aimed at making the anxious and depressed youngsters less fearful and withdrawn, the acting-out or aggressive youngster more socially acceptable, and the "bizarre" youngster more attuned to reality.

In the Spring of 1981, the HRC published a two-year ethnographic study of Unitas, examining its organizational structure and interpersonal processes. The conclusions of this ethnographic study, published in the HRC's sixth monograph called *Unitas: Hispanic and Black Children in a Healing Community,* written by Dr. Anne Farber and Dr. Lloyd H. Rogler, raised the major question of the program's replicability. In order to replicate the program, a vehicle had to be constructed to clearly transmit the program's method. Therefore, as a companion to the monograph, the HRC has developed a logistics manual which presents Unitas techniques in a sequential and integrative manner: *Unitas: A Developmental and Training Manual for Building Healing Communities for Children* (HRC Monograph #8), written by Edward P. Eismann, founder and director of Unitas. This volume has a two-fold purpose: to describe the steps taken historically together with the methods and techniques used in the creation of Unitas as a healing community for children; and to offer the reader a substantive example of the training curriculum given to Unitas teenagers and clinical staff.

On the assumption that it is important to assess the impact of innovative therapeutic modalities, the Hispanic Research Center is conducting an evaluation of the Unitas program. This involves the psychological assessment of the Unitas children to determine how, if at all, they change as a result of their experience in the program. A data-gathering mechanism and structure has been established to collect information on a broad range of dimensions, including demographics, adjustments and attitudes, adaptive behavior, and program participation, all with the goal of compiling a profile of children who participate in Unitas. The study aims to determine the relative contribution of length, frequency, and type of Unitas participation and demographic attributes to potential changes in indices of adjustment, including academic grades, school attendance, and disciplinary infractions. The relative contribution of Unitas participation and several demographic variables to potential changes on selected indices of functioning, e.g., self-esteem and problem-solving ability, is also being examined.

Another response to the urgent need for therapeutic modalities for Hispanics has been the development of folktales as an effective means of ameliorating emotional problems and promoting personality and ego development in children.[265] Gardner[266] has reported that mutual storytelling between therapist and child has resulted in positive therapeutic outcomes in both neurotic and borderline children. In one study involving black and Hispanic children, thematic fantasy play was shown to be associated with a higher incidence of spontaneous play, better story memory, and better storytelling skill.[267] Other investigators have found that storytelling has a positive effect on self-image and empathy in therapeutic contexts.[268] Nevertheless, there is a paucity of experimental literature on the effectiveness of folktale therapy on mental health, although the technique appears to have considerable promise for adaptation to Hispanic cultural experiences.

Folktale or *cuento* therapy, as it is being currently developed by the Hispanic Research Center, is a culture-sensitive treatment modality which bridges the gap between the Puerto Rican cultural heritage and the Anglo culture. Within this model of cuento therapy, the folktales have the function of motivating attentional processes by presenting culturally familiar characters, by modeling characters, thoughts, beliefs and behaviors with which children can identify, and by mediating a more functional relationship with the mother, the storyteller. In addition to the intrinsic human values present in the original folktales, readapted folktales graft into the narrative ego functions from the Anglo culture which promote ego growth. Thus, children who are in conflict between two cultures find a new synthesis and achieve optimal mental health.[269] Cuento therapy promises to be an effective

51

treatment modality with Puerto Rican children and their mothers because it incorporates three cardinal factors: the Puerto Rican heritage as manifested in the folktales; the mother as a pivotal figure in the Puerto Rican family; and adaptive ego functions as reflected in the dominant culture.

In a study of the effectiveness of cuento therapy,[270] Puerto Rican children (grades K-3) and their mothers were screened for behavior problems in a public school setting and then randomly assigned to one of three therapy groups (original Puerto Rican cuento therapy, cuento therapy adapted to American culture, and traditional art-play therapy) versus a control group. Children and their mothers were pre- and posttested with a number of self-report and projective personality tests, intelligence tests, and observational studies. Preliminary findings reveal statistically significant differences between the three therapy groups with respect to therapist-rated improvement in achievement motivation, verbal/cobnitive functioning, and self-concept of competence. In terms of achievement motivation, 86 improvement in adaptiveness of ego functioning, compared to 79 percent in the art-play group, and 60 percent in the adapted cuento group. Similarly, 84 percent of the cuento group was rated as showing adaptive change in verbal/cognitive functioning relative to 81 percent in the adapted cuento group, and 66 percent in the art-play group. Finally, 84 percent of the original cuento children were rated as displaying adaptive change in self-concept compared to 73 percent and 62 percent in the art-play and adapted cuento therapies, respectively. Other statistical comparisons, focused on the original cuento therapy, revealed evidence of moderate differences in therapeutic effectiveness. Overall, a statistically significant percentage (70 percent) of the mothers participating with their children in therapy were rated as demonstrating improvement in adaptiveness of ego functioning.

In sum, research in this phase of the conceptual framework focuses on the ineffectiveness of traditional forms of psychotherapy with Hispanics attributed to confusion and misunderstanding engendered by language barriers, psychocultural distance, socioeconomic bias, reinforcement of alienation, stereotyping, and discrepancies of expectation between Hispanic patients and typically white, middle-class therapists. Such research is urgently needed both to adapt traditional treatment modalities and to develop innovative modalities tailored to the Hispanic culture.

# *Phase 5:*
# POST-TREATMENT REHABILITATION

Phase 5 refers to the post-treatment phase of the clinical services research framework. After a client terminates therapy or a patient leaves a psychiatric hospital, a new set of questions about the effectiveness of treatment comes into focus, questions such as how well he or she will be able to perform major roles, solve problems, and whether or not the continued support of professionals, paraprofessionals, family members, and other persons are needed to sustain the clients as functioning members of the community. At a broader level, questions need to be raised as to the impact of social, structural and cultural factors upon the post-treatment experiences of the client. We shall see that recent historical trends add significance to such questions.

Even though annual admissions to state hospitals increased from 178,000 in 1955 to a peak of 390,000 in 1972 (then decreased to 375,000 in 1974), fully 64 percent of the cases admitted in 1972 were readmissions.[271] The year 1972 also marked the apex of patients released from institutions — over 400,000 — with preceding and subsequent years close in number. The combination of high rates of deinstitutionalization and of readmissions lends credence to Bessuk and Gerson's assertion[272] that despite the promise of treatment and rehabilitation imbedded in the community mental health concept, deinstitutionalization has often meant real hardship and tragedy to the thousands of hospitalized patients released haphazardly "to a non-system of community aftercare." Many of those individuals, discharged after a long period of custodial care, lead a marginal existence in the community, surviving on welfare payments, perhaps receiving some medication or counseling. Unable to cope, they return to the hospital to be maintained on anti-psychotic medication. Goldstein's observation[273] that 85 percent of the patients discharged as a result of deinstitutionalization are located in the socioeconomically lower or working class adds poignancy to the problem. Even though a significant portion of the Hispanic population is economically disadvantaged, we know very little about how all of this affects the post-treatment experience of Hispanic clients.

53

The two measures most often used in assessing the post-treatment level of functioning of clients — in particular, discharged chronic schizophrenics — are rehospitalization and employment. The assumption is that if the individual continues to need institutional support, the number of days hospitalized since discharge and the time which has elapsed before rehospitalization was necessary may reflect the person's ability to cope — provided attention is given to the life situation the person confronts. Being able to maintain a job also is an indication of post-treatment adjustment to the community. The employed individual is less likely to be a financial burden to the family and to society, evidences a capacity for some level of functioning, and is investing effort in a socially desirable activity. Although there is an extensive literature about aftercare and rehabilitation, and although psychotherapy outcome studies often include follow-up measures, attention to the prevention of relapse in recovered Hispanic patients and to their capacity for securing and sustaining employment has largely been nonexistent.[274] At the same time, research has generally neglected the post-treatment experience of Hispanic clients. Our bibliographical efforts indicate that the fifth phase of the five-phase epidemiologic-clinical services research framework has received the least research attention among Hispanic populations. Our discussion, therefore will restrict itself to the following aspects of aftercare: the role of socioeconomic factors, interpersonal relations, employment, and posthospital treatment.

Socioeconomic status, as we have seen in the discussion of Phase 4, plays an important role in clients' experience of the mental health system. Social class continues to be a major factor in what happens after treatment as well. Thus, Zigler and Phillips and their colleagues,[275] using case history data to predict aftercare outcome for discharged schizophrenic patients, found that a high occupational and educational status and a good employment history (and being married) before hospitalization are among the variables which predict good outcome upon discharge. In Meyers and Bean's[276] follow-up study of Hollingshead and Redlich's investigation of social class and mental illness, the deleterious results of being both seriously disturbed and a member of a lower class are strikingly documented. Not only are lower class patients more likely to be readmitted to the hospital, but those patients who remain outside the hospital are more likely than non-lower class patients to experience serious employment difficulties, financial problems, and extreme social isolation. Myers and Bean's thesis is that the lower the social class, the more severely handicapping is the role of the mental patient. The relationship between social class and posthospital adjustment within the Hispanic community remains a matter of empirical determination.

There has been a modicum of attention given to the nature of interpersonal relationships of Hispanic schizophrenics in the community. Amin[277] found that the retention of cultural values by Puerto Rican schizophrenic ex-patients was an important determinant of favorable posthospital adjustment. Classification of patients as retaining or not retaining their cultural values was largely based on the extent of social contacts with family and relatives. Garrison's[278] exploration of the social support systems of schizophrenic and non-schizophrenic Puerto Rican migrant women in New York City pointed to the greater social withdrawal and isolation of the schizophrenic women in comparison to the non-schizophrenics. As the author points out, this finding is unremarkable since the very same characteristics were secondary diagnostic criteria for the schizophrenic group. The data from her study indicate that social withdrawal occurs first from a spouse, then from family (other than parents), then from unrelated persons. She recommends that instead of looking to the family to find support for the chronic schizophrenic patient in relationships that have frequently not been supportive in the past, the clinician might be better advised to encourage voluntary supportive non-kinship relationships. This view is consistent with Leff's[279] position that for discharged patients, contact with families is often deleterious. Rogler and Hollingshead[280] found, however, that severely disturbed schizophrenics in Puerto Rico who had never been hospitalized were able to maintain some viable relationships within their family system, but were less capable of dealing with people and systems outside the family. One might speculate that the discrepancy between the Garrison findings and those of Rogler and Hollingshead may be due to differences in the researchers' respective populations. Rogler and Hollingshead studied individuals who had never been hospitalized and had remained within their families; Garrison studied individuals who had been separated from their families at least during the period of hospitalization. Hospitalization, therefore, may attenuate family bonds. Given the particular importance of family ties within the Hispanic culture, the nature and extent of interpersonal involvement on posthospital adjustment are worthy of careful investigation.

Summers[281] found that recently discharged schizophrenics suffered more from social and vocational dysfunction than from acute symptom distress. Their data indicate that schizophrenics tend to be neurotically symptomatic and socially dysfunctional but not highly psychotic. Lack of performance of social function was evident after the acute phase, and most of the patients were unemployed. Recently, the topic of the relationship between the ex-patient's ability to work and his post-treatment adjustment received attention from Wansbrough and Cooper[282] and from Anthony.[283] Wansbrough and Cooper consider employment a critical variable on several levels: employment is an indication that a person can function at least minimally; it is an aid to rehabilitation; and it is evidence of wellness. In the context of Hispanic social structure and cultural diversity, the meaning and significance of work in interpreting the posthospital experience of clients very likely depend upon the socioeconomic level and the cultural group's normative orientation toward work and other institutional structures. Among Hispanics such issues remain unexamined.

Anthony[284] outlined a variety of post-treatment therapies which have been used in an effort to improve posthospital performance. These include: drug maintenance, aftercare clinics, follow-up counseling, and transitional facilities. From his review, the only modality which emerged as showing a lower rehospitalization rate than no treatment was the aftercare clinic. He raised the point that this group may be self-selected — attendance at a clinic may be an expression of a desire to stay healthy. He also had a favorable evaluation of transitional houses in that, at the very least, they allow the discharged patient to enjoy more freedom and less stigma. From a societal point of view, this type of care is less expensive than maintaining patients in a total institution. This finding could have relevance for Hispanic patients who are among the ranks of those needing aftercare and of those for whom traditional treatment modalities have left much to be desired. An innovative, potentially useful approach to aftercare for low socioeconomic status ex-patients, by implication for some Hispanic groups, may be found in Goldstein's recent work.[285] His starting point is that most of the discharged patients are substantially deficient in important skills necessary for daily functioning. His approach is to teach skills and desirable behavior, because long-term institutionalization renders the patients ill-prepared and vulnerable in the face of community demands following hospital discharge. However, as Wallace et al.[286] caution in their review of the impact of social skills training upon schizophrenic patients, the positive changes do not occur for every patient. And when they do occur, they often do not generalize to new situations. Next to nothing is known about this issue in regard to Hispanic groups.

Although not directed toward Hispanics, research has demonstrated that higher socioeconomic patients who show greater adaptive social and vocational adjustment before hospitalization are most likely to return to the community and conduct a normal social life. In contrast, the majority of the lower socioeconomic status patients languish in dilapidated hotels, rooming houses, halfway houses, and eventually become part of the revolving-door syndrome; that is, they return to be hospitalized over and over again. Although the problems of community adjustment of these patients are great, little research exists on the factors which enhance or suppress their capacity to function.

In sum, the level at which an individual who is no longer in treatment is able to function is the product of factors arrayed across all phases of the conceptual framework. The general neglect of mental health relevant research among Hispanics in all phases of the framework, therefore, makes our ignorance all the more problematical. Specifically, there is a pressing need to focus research upon the fifth phase of the framework to identify factors which enhance or suppress the Hispanics' capacity to function.

# Summary

The need for a comprehensive framework integrating mental health relevant research on Hispanic populations is recognized in the *Report to the President's Commission on Mental Health*. The report notes that the research literature on Hispanic mental health has yet to attain the status of an integrated body of knowledge into which programmatic research could be incorporated. In an effort to remedy the above-noted deficiency, the Hispanic Research Center has developed a framework which views mental health clinical service research on Hispanic populations as spanning a hypothetical temporal sequence. This sequence begins when a person experiences mental or emotional distress and ends after official mental health providers have attempted to deal with the problem and the person attempts to resume his or her customary social roles.

The literature reviewed here indicates the following: studies to determine the mental health of Hispanics are scarce; Hispanics tend to underutilize mental health services in relation to their mental health needs; Hispanics are prone to be misdiagnosed for a variety of reasons; the treatment they receive does not fit their culture or circumstances; and, finally, they are likely to experience difficulty in resuming their customary social roles after undergoing treatment.

Phases 2 through 5 of the framework comprise successive barriers for Hispanics who experience mental health problems, while Phase 1 documents the need for mental health services. Thus, the first phase includes psychiatric epidemiologic studies of Hispanic populations and serves as a foundation for the ensuing phases. The second phase includes studies of the factors influencing the utilization of mental health facilities, such as help-giving indigenous organizations, cultural beliefs in non-traditional forms of therapy, and a host of organizational barriers encountered in the search for therapy. Research in the third phase focuses on the currently prominent issue of cultural insensitivity of traditional assessment procedures for psychodiagnosis and evaluation, and on the effects of bilingualism, language of psychiatric interview, and the ethnicity of the examiner. Research related to the fourth phase focuses on the effectiveness of various forms of psychotherapy with Hispanics, and consequent adaptation of traditional treatment modalities, as well as the development of innovative modalities tailored to Hispanic culture. The fifth phase is of paramount importance, given the recent deinstitutionalization movement of psychiatric patients from mental health facilities to the community and the dearth of knowledge about aftercare, rehabilitation, and recidivism in Hispanic patients.

This framework is not uniquely linked to a specific ethnic group, or to the study of mental health issues. We believe that it can be used profitably to integrate the literature and guide research on any health issue concerning other populations, either minority or majority groups. We invite the use of this framework in contexts other than the mental health area and in non-Hispanic populations.

*Appendix*
# HISPANIC DIVERSITY IN NEW YORK CITY
*By*

**Douglas T. Gurak,**
*Senior Research Associate,*
*Hispanic Research Center and Center for Policy Research*

and

**Lloyd H. Rogler,**
*Director, Hispanic Research Center*
*and Albert Schweitzer Professor of Humanities,*
*Fordham University*

A version of this article appeared in the
*New York University Education Quarterly,* Vol. XI, No. 4, Summer, 1980.

Pope John Paul II's use of Spanish as the second language in the televised mass celebrated at Yankee Stadium in October 1979 pointedly recognized the growing importance of the Hispanic community in the contemporary life of New York City. Conservative estimates indicate that in 1970 about 20 percent of the city's population was Hispanic; in 1980 it was 25 percent. Even though totally reliable numbers are not available, two facts appear to be certain: the absolute and relative size of the Hispanic population continues to increase, and the composition of this population has changed markedly.

Although we base our discussion upon a variety of sources of information, descriptive accounts of this type are necessarily informed guesses. The 1970 census data are out of date, and even when they were collected there were serious problems in the undercounting of minority persons such as Hispanics. Moreover, the Hispanic population includes large numbers of undocumented or illegal immigrants whom it is difficult to interview. Therefore, we have used other sources as well: Board of Education censuses, marriage records, and ethnographic accounts of specific communities, all of which reflect both legal and undocumented immigrants because citizenship or immigration status is not requested. These sources, however, bear more accurately upon specific segments of the Hispanic population. Despite these limitations, selected data from these sources are brought together in this account.

The 1970 census counted 811,843 Puerto Ricans living in New York City and a half-million other Hispanics, but the latter number is a very low estimate due to undercount problems. Although evidence indicates that more Puerto Ricans have been leaving the city in the last decade than entering it, close to one million Puerto Ricans remain, and they are still the predominant Hispanic group. It is, however, the non-Puerto Rican Hispanic population that has been growing rapidly.[1] For example, during the 1970's approximately 12,600 Dominicans per year immigrated legally to the United States, the vast majority settling in New York City.[2] The flow of undocumented migrants appears to be much higher, but precise estimates are not available. One informed estimate states that 300,000 Dominicans live in the United States with the substantial majority residing in New York City.[3]

Even though official statistical sources tend to classify all non-Puerto Rican Hispanics into one group, large numbers of Cubans, Peruvians, Ecuadorians, and other South-Central Americans live in the city. In particular, there are large numbers of Dominicans and Colombians: about 20 percent of the Hispanics who married in the city in 1975 were from South American countries; another 13 percent were Dominicans; 8 percent were from Central American countries; and 4 percent were Cubans.

These same marriage records, which provide the best available official data, demonstrate considerable variation in socioeconomic composition and distinct Hispanic communities. Puerto Ricans constitute the numerically dominant Hispanic group in all boroughs except Queens, where the South Americans, with 43 percent of the Hispanic population, are numerically superior. The largest Puerto Rican communities exist in the Bronx and in Brooklyn. The largest Dominican communities are in the Upper West Side and Washington Heights areas of Manhattan and in Corona, Queens. There are South American colonies of significant size in the north-central Queens communities of Jackson Heights, Elmhurst, and Woodside.[4] Cubans and Central Americans tend toward a more even dispersion throughout the city, though both are disproportionately located in Manhattan. A large proportion of Central Americans reside in Brooklyn, and Cubans in Queens.

## Socioeconomic Character

The socioeconomic status of Hispanics of different national origins varies considerably at both the national level and within New York City. Cubans and South-Central Americans (not including Mexican Americans at the national level) have relatively high levels of education and high-status occupations. It was the upper-middle class and middle class that fled from

Castro's Cuba, and, in the case of South America, it is persons with resources who tend to emigrate and who can afford the journey. Puerto Ricans and Dominicans (and Mexicans at the national level), on the other hand, coming from a closer proximity and from less economically advanced areas, rank relatively low in education and in the status of their occupations.

New York City marriage records contain information on the occupations of both brides and grooms, though other data on socioeconomic status are not collected. Cuban men have relatively high-status occupations in the city, as they do in the nation as a whole: 19 percent hold professional or managerial positions, and another 35 percent are in white-collar positions. Dominicans and Puerto Ricans have the lowest-status positions. Only 7.7 percent of Dominican grooms and 9.8 of Puerto Rican grooooms have professional or managerial positions, with over half in each group located in low-skill blue-collar or service positions. The occupational distributions of South and Central Americans more closely approximate those of Cubans than those of Dominicans and Puerto Ricans.

The situation for brides is essentially the same, except that significantly fewer brides listed any occupation: 48.5 percent of Puerto Rican brides listed no occupation, as did 31.6 percent of the Cuban and 37.4 percent of the Dominican women.[5] The data conform to numerous other studies of female labor force participation. Most groups have high levels of participation, with the exception of Puerto Rican women, who have a low level of employment.[6] While only partial, these figures and other data on the socio-economic status of the various Hispanic groups of New York City parallel the Hispanic national pattern.

We must keep in mind that the occupational status of immigrant populations tends to underestimate the human resources that the immigrants bring with them. The reasons for this are complex; they include such basic factors as language barriers and assorted disruptions brought on by the process of migration. Also, an unknown proportion of migrants work in the peripheral sector of the economy that offers low wages, no job security, and little opportunity for promotion, their goal being to maximize earnings for a return migration rather than to build a career. Considerable data support the claim that Hispanic migrants experience some downward mobility upon entering the host society. Moreover, the tendency to stereotype Hispanic immigrants as peasants with little training is wrong, even for the relatively poor Dominican immigrants. Two recent studies of international migrant Dominican families demonstrate that they tend to be relatively well-educated, disproportionately urban, and modern, when compared to the non-migrant component of the Dominican population.[7]

With the exception of Puerto Rican brides and grooms, second-generation Hispanics have markedly higher-status occupations than the first. Whereas only 7.4 percent of first-generation Dominican grooms had professional or managerial positions, that figure rises to 20.5 percent in the second generation. South and Central Americans experience similarly dramatic increases. The already large Cuban percentage in the high-status jobs in the first generation probably accounts for the small generational increase they experience. However, the relatively low status of first-generation Puerto Ricans is only marginally improved in the second generation. Generation-of-residence in the U.S. is strongly related to assimilation as well as to occupational status for Hispanic groups, but Puerto Ricans tend not to follow the general trend of assimilation.[8]

## Social Welfare Problems

Only selected aspects of the social welfare problems of Hispanics in New York City can be discussed because statistics generally describe only the Puerto Rican population or some poorly specified Hispanic population. The socioeconomic and residential diversities of the Hispanic populations strongly indicate that housing, health, and other social welfare conditions vary considerably.

Because a significant, if unknown, proportion of non-Puerto Rican, non-Cuban Hispanics are illegal or improperly documented immigrants, special social welfare problems exist. Individuals who fear detection or lack appropriate identification will find it more difficult to take advantage of existing services.[9] Some hospitals in the city require identification of citizenship or immigrant status prior to administering emergency services. Undocumented migrants do use some services, but we know next to nothing about the extent of this use, or about the implications of illegal status for the welfare of Hispanic individuals.

Poor immigrants in general, and improperly documented ones in particular, are in no position to complain about substandard wages or poor working conditions. Similarly, they are in no position to search carefully for the best possible employment and, therefore, are quite likely to work at least some time in the lower paying, insecure jobs provided by the marginal, underground industries of the city.[10] For example, the availability of jobs in the garment and restaurant industries and in domestic service stimulates the flow of international migrants:[11] At present, our knowledge concerning the actual employment experiences of most legal or illegal Hispanic immigrants is so sparce that we cannot determine the magnitude of exploitation in the labor market. We believe it is not trivial. Employment in the peripheral or secondary sector entails a lack of participation in health plans, retirement plans, and other job-related benefits.

One review of the health needs of the city's Puerto Rican population documented very high rates of drug abuse, lead poisoning, cirrhosis of the liver, and accident- and homicide-related deaths, as well as poor representation of Hispanics at the delivery end of the health system. Because a similar situation prevails for blacks, the health problems seem to be related to conditions of general poverty. The barriers to adequate health care appear to be structural in character: physicians do not locate practices in areas where the poor tend to live, and hospital staff at the treatment and administrative levels remain disproportionately non-Hispanic, even more so than non-black.[12] Such distributions erect a communication barrier of language difference and differing cultural conceptions of illness, particularly of when it is appropriate to seek professional help.

A study of the Hispanic experience of criminal justice in New York City describes the increasing overrepresentation of Hispanics in New York State and federal prisons.[13] The study also considers the question of whether or not the Hispanic offenders' collective experience is different from that of other ethnic-group members being processed through the criminal justice system. Data from a federal court reveal that being Hispanic increases the probability that the offender will be convicted of a drug offense; decreases the probability of being placed on probation; increases the probability of being sent to prison; and increases the probability of a longer sentence, if placed on probation. Of singular importance is the finding that ethnicity interacts with the system in such a way that even when analytical controls are imposed upon the character of the offense, Hispanics are more likely to be sent to prison and to receive harsher sentences.

## Bilingualism

The size of New York's Hispanic population has meant that much social and economic life goes on without the use of English. Two UHF television stations function primarily in Spanish; three radio stations broadcast in Spanish; two large-distribution daily newspapers publish in Spanish; numerous periodicals from Puerto Rico and several Hispanic countries are flown in and distributed throughout the city on a daily basis. Many commercial enterprises are run by Hispanics, and many others have begun to seek the Hispanic market by advertising in Spanish and providing Spanish-language services — a process which reflects the large numbers of Hispanics in the labor force.

Nevertheless, serious debate has emerged over the roles of English and Spanish in institutions such as the courts, polling booths, and the schools. Nowhere has the issue of bilingualism been so important as in the schools. Several studies have indicated that children who were born on the mainland or began school here at an early age have few problems in school stemming from a language barrier.[14] Large numbers of non-English-speaking students, however, are entering the school system in mid-career and language barriers constitute an important problem. Correlatively, data indicate that of every hundred Puerto Rican pupils who enter high school, only about thirty graduate.[15]

Hispanics are not well represented in professional positions in the New York City public school system. For example, in the 1968-1969 school year,

21.5 percent of the system's pupils but only 0.8 percent of the teachers were Puerto Rican. A significant discrepancy remains despite a dramatic increase in the hiring of Hispanic teachers during the 1970's. The impact of programs initiated by the Bilingual Education Act in 1968 to assist pupils with limited English-speaking ability remains unclear, while the extent and nature of this effort continue to be volatile political issues.

## Impact on the City

The growing importance of the Spanish language and developments in the mass media and the schools have done much to alter the character of the city. One could argue, however, that the primary impact of the growth of the Hispanic population has been economic. Some say that the large illegal immigrant component caused unemployment among U.S. citizens and among legal immigrants; others say that migrant labor, legal and illegal, is filling jobs that other persons do not want or that could not exist if wages had to be raised. This would mean that marginal industries — like the garment and restaurant industries — are being kept alive by migrants and providing much broader economic benefits through a multiplier effect.[16] Official and scholarly data are so poor, however, that neither position, nor any intermediate one, can be decisively supported or refuted. We do know that though a large number of Hispanic immigrants are in marginal, low-paying jobs, Hispanics are serving a wide range of economic functions.[17]

## Assimilation

A significant portion of New York's Hispanics are becoming long-term residents of this country despite the often repeated theme that their stay is temporary; assimilation processes are well under way. As time passes some immigrants find better jobs, make financial commitments, marry non-immigrants, or form families that enmesh them in locally based reciprocal obligations. One measure is Hispanic enrollment in the senior colleges of the City University of New York, which has leaped 500 percent in the last decade and now is just under 15 percent of the school's total enrollment.

Another measure of assimilation is the relatively large number of Hispanics who are marrying in the city. Many Hispanics have married Hispanics from countries other than their own: Puerto Ricans have married Dominicans, for example. A surprisingly large proportion of the marriages, however, have involved non-Hispanics — from a low of 6 percent for all Dominican grooms to a high of 32.5 for all Cuban grooms. The percentage of second-generation Hispanics marrying non-Hispanics ranges from the Puerto Rican grooms' low of 8.1 percent to a high of 63.9 percent for Central American brides. Among non-Puerto Rican second-generation

Hispanics the lowest rate of intermarriage with non-Hispanics is the 32.4 percent rate of Dominican brides. Marital assimilation means that a high level of intergroup activity is occurring and that there is increasing commitment to permanent settlement.

Perhaps the most striking aspect about the recent research on New York's Hispanic populations is the accumulating evidence that Puerto Ricans are lagging in terms of assimilation and in terms of economic competition. In addition to the low marital assimilation pattern and the decline in female labor force participation referred to above, numerous sources indicate that, relative to other groups in New York and in U.S. society, Puerto Ricans are falling behind in terms of income. For example, between 1959 and 1969, real income of New York Puerto Rican families increased 13 percent, while that of blacks and of the total city population increased 26 and 23 percent, respectively. Data for the country as a whole indicate that this economic slippage is occurring outside of the city also. In 1969, 28 percent of Puerto Rican families and 13 percent of majority population (non-Hispanic white) families were below the poverty level. By 1976 the Puerto Rican rate had risen to 32 percent while the majority population rate declined to 9 percent. Much of this pattern can be attributed to the relatively rapid increase of female-headed households among Puerto Ricans, since Puerto Rican husband-wife-headed families appeared to have kept up with others. This focuses our attention on social and economic forces impacting on the Puerto Rican family. Among recent immigrant groups, only the Dominican family has a similarly high proportion of single-parent households. Despite this similarity to the pattern found for Puerto Ricans, it is too early to conclude that their social, economic and assimilation experiences will parallel those of Puerto Ricans.[18] One fact is certain: Puerto Ricans have been experiencing severe social and economic stresses. The facts relevant to diversity indicate the need for distinguishing among Hispanic groups for purposes of public policy and for our own general understanding.[19]

## Notes

1. Wagenheim, K.

1975      *A Survey of Puerto Ricans on the U.S. Mainland in the 1970's*. New York: Praeger. Pp. 39-40. The Board of Education's ethnic census in 1977 found 30 percent of the system's pupils to be Hispanic. The 304,327 pupils identified as Hispanic represent the minimum estimate of Hispanic pupils because the census did not carefully identify non-Puerto Rican Hispanics. Of the 123,062 persons who married in 1975 in New York City, 22.5 percent were Hispanic. In turn, 44.2 percent of the Hispanics, or 12,261 persons, were not Puerto Rican; rather, they were Dominicans,

Colombians, Cubans, and persons representing other South and Central American countries.

2. U.S. Department of Justice
1978    *Immigration and Naturalization 1976 Annual Report.* Washington, D.C.: U.S. Government Printing Office.

3. Ugalde, A.; Bean, F.D.; and Cardenas, A.
1979    International Migration from the Dominican Republic: Findings from a National Survey. *International Migration Review* 13, 2 (Summer): 235-54.

4. Sassen-Koob, S.K.
1979    Formal and Informal Associations: Dominicans and Colombians in New York City. *International Migration Review* 13, 2 (Summer): 314-32.

5. Fitzpatrick,.J. and Gurak, D.T.
1979    *Hispanic Intermarriage in New York City: 1975,* Hispanic Research Center Monograph No. 2. Bronx, New York: Fordham University.

6. Cooney, R.S. and Colon, A.W.
1979    Declining Female Participation among Puerto Rican New Yorkers: A Comparison with Native White Non-Spanish New Yorkers. *Ethnicity* 6 (September): 281-297.

Cooney, R.S.
1979    Intercity Variations in Puerto Rican Female Labor Force Participation. *Human Resources* 19 (Spring): 225-35.

7. Ugalde et al., *op. cit.,* Note 3.

Gurak, D.T.
1979    Women in Santo Domingo: Implications for Understanding New York's Dominican Population. Fordham University *Hispanic Research Center Bulletin* 2 (3): 4-5.

Gurak, D.T. and Kritz, M.M.
1982 .    Settlement and Integration Processes of Dominicans and Colombians in New York City. Paper presented at the Annual Meeting of the American Sociological Association, September, San Francisco.

8. Many people assume that Hispanics are a high-fertility group. In fact, with the exception of Mexican Americans and Puerto Ricans, the average fertility levels of other Hispanics — Cubans, South Americans, Central

Americans — in the U.S. are among the lowest in the world. Even Puerto Rican fertility exceeds the national average only slightly. See Douglas T. Gurak, Sources of Ethnic Fertility Differences: An Examination of Five Minority Groups. *Social Science Quarterly,* September 1978, pp. 295-310.

9. U.S. Congress, House Select Committee on Population.
1978    *Legal and Illegal Immigration to the United States.* Washington, D.C.: U.S. Government Printing Office.

Keeley, C.B.
1979    *U.S. Immigration: A Political Analysis.* New York: Population Council.

10. Buck, R.
1979    The New Sweatshops: A Penny for Your Collar. *New York,* January, pp. 40-46.

de Dios Unnane, M.
1979    Salvadoreña Relata Odisea Fabricas N.Y. *El Diario-La Prensa,* November 1, p. 3.

11. Beck, E.M.; Horan, P.M.; and Tolbert, C.M. III
1978    Stratifications in the Dual Economy. *American Sociological Review* 43 (5): 704-720.

Portes, A. and Bach, R.L.
1979    Dual Labor Markets and Immigration: A Test of Competing Theories of Income Inequality. Mimeographed. Durham, N.C.: Duke University Center for International Studies.

The lack of attention given to different family structures and patterns of seeking help in an Hispanic group — Puerto Ricans — and in the dominant groups, is documented in L.H. Rogler, Help Patterns, the Family, and Mental Health: Puerto Ricans in the United States. *International Migration Review* 12 (2): 248-259.

12. Alers, J.O.
1978    *Puerto Ricans and Health: Findings from New York City.* Hispanic Research Center Monograph No. 1. Bronx, N.Y.: Fordham University.

13. Sissons, P.
1979    *The Hispanic Experience of Criminal Justice.* Hispanic Research Center Monograph No. 3. Bronx, N.Y.: Fordham University.

Tuchman, G.
1979     Let's Hold Trials Here in Spanish. *The New York Times,*
August 28.

**14.** Rogler, L.H. and Cooney, R.S.
1979     Intergenerational Change in Ethnic Identity in the Puerto
Rican Family. Paper presented at annual meeting of the American
Sociological Association, Boston, Mass., August.

**15.** Olmedo, E.L. and Lopez, S.
1977     *Hispanic Mental Health Professionals.* Spanish-Speaking
Mental Health Research Center Monograph No. 5. Los Angeles: University
of California, p. 27.

Recent reports indicate dropout rates are much higher in New York City
than elsewhere in the country: F.M. Hechinger, What Can be Done about
Dropouts?, *The New York Times,* October 23, 1979.

**16.** Economic Development Council of New York City.
1977     *The Illegal Alien and the Economy.* New York: Economic
Development Council.

U.S. Congress, *op. cit.,* Note 9.

**17.** Gurak, D.T. and Kritz, M.M., *op. cit.,* Note 7.

Gurak, D.T. and Kritz,M.M.
1982     Dominican and Colombian Women in New York City:
Household Structure and Employment Patterns. *Migration Today* 10, 3/4,
Fall.

Gurak, D.T.
1980     Hispanic Immigrants in New York: Work Settlement, and
Adjustment. National Institute of Mental Health. Supported Research.

**18.** Gurak, D.T. and Kritz, M.M., *op. cit.,* Note 7.

**19.** U.S. Department of Labor
1975     *A Socioeconomic Profile of Puerto Rican New Yorkers.* New
York: U.S. Department of Labor, Middle Atlantic Regional Office, p. 11.

U.S. Commission on Civil Rights
1978     *Social Indicators of Equality for Minorities and Women.*
Washington, D.C.: U.S. Government Printing Office. p. 62.

# REFERENCES

1. Padilla, A. and Ruiz, R.
   1973      *Latino Mental Health: A Review of the Literature.* DHEW Publication No. (HSM) 73-9143. Washington, D.C.: U.S. Government Printing Office.

2. Special Populations Sub-Task Panel on Mental Health of Hispanic Americans
   1978      *Report to the President's Commission on Mental Health.* Los Angeles: Spanish Speaking Mental Health Research Center, University of California, p. 4.

3. Gurak, D.T. and Rogler, L.H.
   1980a      Hispanic Diversity in New York City. *Hispanic Research Center Research Bulletin* 3 (3): 1-5.

   Zavaleta, A.N.
   1981      Variations in Hispanic Health Status. *Hispanic Research Center Research Bulletin* 4 (2-3): 1-6.

   Gurak, D.T.
   1981      Family Structural Diversity of Hispanic Ethnic Groups. *Hispanic Research Center Research Bulletin* 4 (2-3): 6-10.

   Alvirez, D.
   1981      Socioeconomic Patterns and Diversity among Hispanics. *Hispanic Research Center Research Bulletin* 4 (2-3): 11-14.

4. Hispanic Research Center
   1981      Progress Report. *Hispanic Research Center Research Bulletin* 4 (1).

5. Hollingshead, A.B. and Redlich, F.C.
1958    *Social Class and Mental Illness.* New York: John Wiley and Sons.

6. Kohn, M.
1968    Social Class and Schizophrenia: A Critical Review. In D. Rosenthal and S.S. Kety (eds.), *The Transmission of Schizophrenia.* Oxford: Pergamon Press.

1972    Class, Family, and Schizophrenia: A Reformulation. *Social Forces* 50 (3): 295-313.

7. Faris, R. and Dunham, N.
1939    *Mental Disorders in Urban Areas.* Chicago: University of Chicago Press.

Jaco, E.
1960    *The Social Epidemiology of Mental Disorders: A Psychiatric Survey of Texas.* New York: Russell Sage Foundation.

Kleiner, R. and Parker, S.
1959    Migration and Mental Illness: A New Look. *American Sociological Review* 25 (5): 687-690.

Krupinski, J.
1967    Sociological Aspects of Mental Ill Health in Migrants. *Social Science and Medicine* 1: 267-281.

Lazarus, J.; Locke, B.; and Thomas, D.
1963    Migration Differentials in Mental Disease: State Patterns in First Admission to Mental Hospitals for All Disorders and for Schizophrenia: New York, Ohio, California, as of 1950. *Milbank Memorial Fund Quarterly* 41: 25-42.

Lee, E.
1963    Socioeconomic and Migration Differentials in Mental Disease, New York State, 1949-61. *Milbank Memorial Fund Quarterly* 41: 249-268.

Malzberg, B.
1962    *The Mental Health of the Negro: A Study of First Admissions to Hospitals for Mental Disease in New York State, 1949-51.* Albany: Research Foundation for Mental Hygiene.

1964    Mental Disease among Native Whites and Foreign-Born Whites in New York State, 1949-51. *Mental Hygiene* 48: 478-499.

Malzberg, B.
1969        Are Immigrants Psychologically Disturbed? In S. Plog and R. Edgerton (eds.), *Changing Perspectives in Mental Illness.* New York: Holt, Rinehart, and Winston.

Malzberg, B. and Lee, E.
1956        *Migration and Mental Disease: A Study of First Admissions to Hospitals for Mental Disease, New York, 1939-41.* New York: Social Science Research Council.

Mintz, N. and Schwartz, D.
1964        Urban Ecology and Psychosis. *International Journal of Social Psychiatry* 10: 101-118.

Murphy, H.B.
1965        Migration and the Major Mental Disorders: A Reappraisal. In Kantor, M.B. (ed.), *Mobility and Mental Health.* Springfield, Illinois: Charles C. Thomas.

Odegaarde, O.
1932        Emigration and Insanity: A Study of Mental Disease among the Norwegian-Born Population in Minnesota. *Acta Psychiatrica et Neurologica, Scandanavia,* Suppl. 4: 1-206.

8. Sanua, V.
1970        Immigration, Migration and Mental Illness: A Review of the Literature with Special Emphasis on Schizophrenia. In E. Brody (ed.), *Behavior in New Environments: Adaptation of Migrant Populations* (2nd ed.). Beverly Hills: Sage Publications.

9. Jaco, E., *op. cit.,* Note 7.

Kleiner, R. and Parker, S., 1959, *op. cit.,* Note 7.

Kleiner, R. and Parker, S.
1965        Goal Striving and Psychosomatic Symptoms in a Migrant and Non-Migrant Population. In M. Kantor (ed.), *Mobility and Mental Health.* Springfield, Illinois: Charles C. Thomas.

1970        Social-Psychological Aspects of Migration and Mental Disorder in a Negro Population. In E. Brody (ed.), *op. cit.,* Note 8.

Krupinski, J., *op. cit.,* Note 7.

Kuo, W.

1976    Theories of Migration and Mental Health: An Empirical Testing of Chinese Americans. *Social Science and Medicine* 10 (6): 297-306.

Lazarus, S. et al., *op. cit.,* Note 7.

Malzberg, B., 1969, *op. cit.,* Note 7.

Parker, S. and Kleiner, R.
1966    *Mental Illness in an Urban Negro Community.* Glencoe, Illinois: The Free Press.

Parker, S.; Kleiner, R.; and Needelman, B.
1969    Migration and Mental Illness: Some Reconsiderations and Suggestions for Further Analysis. *Social Science and Medicine* 3 (1): 1-19.

10. Kleiner, R., and Parker, S., 1965, 1970, *op. cit.,* Note 9.

Krupinski, J., *op. cit.,* Note 7.

Lazarus, J. et al., *op. cit.,* Note 7.

Malzberg, B., 1963, 1969, *op. cit.,* Note 7.

Malzberg, B. and Lee, E., *op. cit.,* Note 7.

Mintz, N. and Schwartz, D., *op. cit.,* Note 7.

11. Faris, R. and Dunham, N., *op. cit.,* Note 7.

Freedman, R.
1950    *Recent Migration to Chicago.* Chicago: University of Chicago Press.

Jaco, E., *op. cit.,* Note 7.

Lazarus, J. et al., *op. cit.,* Note 7.

Malzberg, B.
1960    *Mental Disease Among Jews in New York State.* New York: Intercontinental Medical Book Corp.

Malzberg, B., 1963, *op. cit.,* Note 7.

Odegaarde, O., *op. cit.,* Note 7.

12. Rendon, M.
    1974        Transcultural Aspects of Puerto Rican Mental Illness in New York. *International Journal of Social Psychiatry* 20: 18-24.

13. Hispanic Research Center, *op. cit.,* Note 4.

14. Canino, I.; Earley, B.; and Rogler, L.H.
    1980        *The Puerto Rican Child in New York City: Stress and Mental Health*. Bronx, N.Y.: Hispanic Research Center, Fordham University (Monograph 4).

15. Roberts, R.
    1980        Prevalence of Psychological Distress among Mexican Americans. *Journal of Health and Social Behavior* 21 (2): 134-145.

16. *Ibid.,* p. 141.

17. Srole, L.; Langner, T.; Michael, S.; Opler, M.; and Rennic, T.
    1962        *Mental Health in the Metropolis: The Midtown Manhattan Study*. New York: McGraw Hill.

18. Dohrenwend, B.P.
    1966        Social Status and Psychological Disorder: An Issue of Substance and an Issue of Method. *American Sociological Review* 31: 14-34.

19. Dohrenwend, B.P. and Dohrenwend, B.S.
    1969        *Social Status and Psychological Disorder: A Causal Inquiry*. New York: John Wiley and Sons.

20. Padilla, A.M.; Ruiz, R.A.; and Alvarez, R.
    1975        Community Mental Health Services for the Spanish-Speaking Surnamed Population. *American Psychologist* 30 (September): 892-905.

21. Piore, M.
    1979        *Birds of Passage: Migrant Labor in Industrial Society*. Cambridge: Cambridge University Press.

    Garrison, V. and Weiss, C.I.
    1979        Dominican Family Networks and United States Immigration Policy: A Case Study. *International Migration Review,* 13 (2): 264-283.

22. Fitzpatrick, J.P. and Gurak, D.T.
    1979        *Hispanic Intermarriage in New York City: 1975*. Bronx, New York: Hispanic Research Center, Fordham University (Monograph No. 2).

Gurak, D.T. and Rogler, L.H., 1980a, *op. cit.*, Note 3.

Gurak, D.T. and Rogler, L.H.
1980b    New York's New Immigrants: Who and Where They Are. The Hispanics. *New York University Education Quarterly,* 11 (4): 20-24.

Zavaleta, A.N., *op. cit.*, Note 3.

Gurak, D.T., *op. cit.*, Note 3.

Alvirez, D., *op. cit.*, Note 3.

23. Coates, D.B.; Moyer, S.; Kendall, L.; and Howat, M.G.
1976    Life-Event Changes and Mental Health. In I.G. Sarason and C.D. Spielberger (eds.), *Stress and Anxiety,* Vol. 3. New York: John Wiley and Sons.

Gray, J. A.
1976    The Neuropsychology of Anxiety. In *Ibid.*

Epstein, S.
1976    Anxiety, Arousal, and the Self-Concept. In *Ibid.*

Rule, B.G. and Nesdale, A.R.
1976    Environmental Stressors, Emotional Arousal, and Aggression. In *Ibid.*

Menninger, K.
1945    *The Human Mind* (3rd ed.). New York: Alfred A. Knopf.

Boehm, W.W.
1955    The Role of Psychiatric Social Work in Mental Health. In A.M. Rose (ed.), *Mental Health and Mental Disorders.* New York: W.W. Norton.

Buss, A.H.
1966    *Psychopathology.* New York: John Wiley and Sons.

McLean, P.D.
1976    Depression as a Specific Response to Stress. In I.G. Sarason and C.D. Spielberger (eds.), *op. cit.*, Note 23.

Keezer, W.S.
1971    *Mental and Human Behavior.* Dubuque, Iowa: W.C. Brown, Publisher.

Rosenberg, M.
1965        Self-Esteem and Anxiety. In *Society and the Adolescent Self-Image*. Princeton, New Jersey: Princeton University Press.

24. Reubens, P.
1980        Psychological Needs of the New Immigrants. *Migration Today* 8 (2): 8-14.

25. Struening, E.L.; Rabkin, J.G.; and Peck. H.B.
1969        Migration and Ethnic Membership in Relation to Social Problems. In E.B. Brody (ed.), *Behavior in New Environments: Adaptation of Migrant Populations* (1st Ed.). Beverly Hills: Sage Publications.

Morrison, S.D.
1973        Intermediate Variables in the Association Between Migration and Mental Illness. *International Journal of Social Psychiatry* 19 (1-2): 60-65.

Verdonk, A.
1979        Migration and Mental Illness. *International Journal of Social Psychiatry* 25 (4): 295-305.

26. Mills, C.W.; Senior, C.; and Goldsen, R.K.
1950        *The Puerto Rican Journey: New York's Newest Migrants*. New York: Harper and Row, pp. 68-70.

Rogg, E.M. and Cooney, R.S.
1980        *Adaption and Adjustment of Cubans: West·New York, New Jersey*. Bronx, N.Y.: Hispanic Research Center, Fordham University (Monograph No. 5), pp. 35-46.

Gurak, D.T. and Rogler, L.H., *op. cit.*, Note 3.

27. Aneshensel, C.S.; Frerichs, R.R.; and Clark, V.A.
1981        Family Roles and Sex Differences in Depression. *Journal of Health and Social Behavior* 22 (4): 379-393.

28. Padilla, A.M.
1980        The Role of Cultural Awareness and Ethnic Loyalty in Acculturation. In A.M. Padilla (ed.), *Acculturation: Theory, Models and Some New Findings*. Boulder, Colorado: Westview Press.

29. Fabrega, H., Jr. and Wallace, C.A.
1968        Value Identification and Psychiatric Disability: An Analysis Involving Americans of Mexican Descent. *Behavioral Science* 13 (5): 362-371.

Kuo, W., *op. cit.*, Note 9.

Szapocznik, J. and Kurtines, W.
1980    Acculturation, Biculturalism, and Adjustment Among Cuban-Americans. In A.M. Padilla (ed.), *Acculturation, Theory, Models and Some New Findings*. Boulder, Colorado: Westview Press.
Torres-Matrullo, C.M.
1976    Acculturation and Psychopathology among Puerto Rican Women in Mainland United States. *American Journal of Orthopsychiatry* 46 (4): 710-719.

1980    Acculturation, Sex Role Values, and Mental Health among Mainland Puerto Ricans. In A.M. Padilla (ed.), *op. cit.*, Note 28.

Verdonk, A., *op. cit.*, Note 25.

30. Lang, J.
1982    Latinos in San Francisco: An Investigation into Acculturation, Quality of Life, and Well-Being of Hispanics Residing in a Bicultural Urban Environment of the United States. Paper presented at the Multi-Ethnic Conference on Assessment, Tampa, Florida, (March 7-10).

Szapocznik, J. and Kurtines, W., *op. cit.*, Note 29.

31. Rogler, L.H. and Cooney, R.S.
1975    Help Patterns in Intergenerational Puerto Rican Families. Grant application submitted to National Institute of Mental Health, #1 RO1 MH28314-01.

32. Lash, T.; Sigal, H.; and Dudzinski, D.
1979    *Children and Families in New York City: An Analysis of the 1976 Survey of Income and Education*. New York: Foundation for Child Development.

Canino, I.A.; Earley, B.F.; and Rogler, L.H., *op. cit.*, Note 14.

National Puerto Rican Forum
1980    *The Next Step Toward Equality: A Comprehensive Study of Puerto Ricans in the United States Mainland*. New York: National Puerto Rican Forum, p. 10.

33. U.S. Bureau of the Census
1978    Persons of Spanish Origin in the United States: March 1977. *Current Population Reports*, Series P-20, No. 329. Washington, D.C.: U.S. Government Printing Office.

34. U.S. Bureau of Census
    1980    Persons of Spanish Origin in the United States: March 1979. *Current Population Reports,* Series P-20, No. 354. Washington, D.C.: U.S. Government Printing Office.

    Tienda, Marta (ed.)
    1981    Market Structure and Earnings Determination of Native and Immigrant Hispanics in the United States. In *Hispanic Origin Workers in the U.S. Labor Market.* Final report submitted to the U.S. Department of Labor (October).

35. Pearlin, L.I.; Lieberman, M.A.; Menaghan, E.G.; and Mullan, J.T.
    1981    The Stress Process. *Journal of Health and Social Behavior,* 22 (4): 337-356.

36. Kobasa, S.C.; Maddi, S.R.; and Courington, S.
    1981    Personality and Constitution as Mediators in the Stress-Illness Relationship. *Journal of Health and Social Behavior,* 22 (4): 368-378.

37. Rogler, L.H. and Hollingshead, A.B.
    1975    *Trapped: Families and Schizophrenia* (2nd edition). New York: Krieger Publishing Company.

38. Paykel, E.S.
    1974    Life Stress and Psychiatric Disorder: Applications of the Clinical Approach. In B.P. Dohrenwend and B.S. Dohrenwend (eds.) *Stressful Life Events: Their Nature and Effects.* New York: John Wiley and Sons.

39. Lauer, R.H.
    1973    The Social Readjustment Scale and Anxiety: *A Cross-Cultural Study. Journal of Psychosomatic Research* 17: 171-174.

40. Brown, G. and Girley, J..
    1968    Crises and Life Changes and the Onset of Schizophrenia. *Journal of Health and Social Behavior* 9: 203-214.

    Rogler, L.H. and Hollingshead, A.B., 1975, *op. cit.,* Note 37.

41. Fontana, A.; Marcus. J.; Noel, B.; and Rakusin, Jr.
    1972    Prehospitalization Coping Styles of Psychiatric Patients: The Goal-Directedness of Life Events. *Journal of Nervous and Mental Disease* 155: 311-321.

42. Paykel, E.S., *op. cit.,* Note 38.

**43.** Myers, J.; Lindenthal, J.; and Pepper, M.
1971    Life Events and Psychiatric Impairment. *Journal of Nervous and Mental Disease* 152: 149-157.

**44.** Mueller, D.P.; Edwards, D.W.; and Yarvis, R.W.
1977    Stressful Life Events and Psychiatric Symptomatology: Change or Undesirability? *Journal of Health and Social Behavior* 18 (3): 307-317.

**45.** Pearlin, L.I. et al., *op. cit.,* Note 35, p. 345.

**46.** Catalano, R. and Dooley, C.D.
1977    Economic Predictors of Depressed Mood and Stressful Life Events in a Metropolitan Community. *Journal of Health and Social Behavior* 18 (3): 292-307.

**47.** Kobasa, S. et al., *op. cit.,* Note 36.

**48.** Pearlin, L.I. et al., *op. cit.,* Note 35, p. 341.

**49.** Rogler, L.H. and Hollingshead, A.B., 1975, *op. cit.,* Note 37.

**50.** Wakefield, D.
1959    *Island in the City: The World of Spanish Harlem.* Boston: Houghton Mifflin Co.

Garrison, V.
1977    Doctor, *Espiritista* or Psychiatrist? Health-Seeking Behavior in a Puerto Rican Neighborhood of New York City. *Medical Anthropology* 1 (2).

Harwood, A.
1977    *Rx: Spiritist as Needed. A Study of a Puerto Rican Community Mental Health Resource.* New York: John Wiley and Sons.

**51.** Bram, J.
1958    Spirits, Mediums, and Believers in Contemporary Puerto Rico. *Transcripts of the New York Academy of Science* 20: 340-347.

**52.** Pearlin, L.I. et al., *op. cit.,* Note 35.

**53.** Durkheim, E.
1951    *Suicide: A Study in Sociology.* Translated by J.A. Spaulding and G. Simpson. New York: The Free Press.

**54.** Gurak, D.T. and Rogler, L.H.

    1983      Hispanic Migrants in New York Settlement. Renewal application submitted to the Department of Health and Human Services, Washington, D.C.

**55.** Kessler, R.

    1982      A Disaggregation of the Relationship Between Socioeconomic Status and Psychological Distress. *American Sociological Review* 47 (6): 752-764.

**56.** Bachrach, L.

    1975      *Utilization of State and County Mental Hospitals by Spanish-Americans in 1972.* NIMH Division of Biometry, Statistical Note 116, DHEW Publication No. (ADM) 75-158. Washington, D.C.: U.S. Government Printing Office.

**57.** National Institute of Mental Health

    1980      *Hispanic Americans and Mental Health Facilities: A Comparison of Hispanic, Black, and White Admissions to Selected Mental Health Facilities, 1975.* Series CN, No. 3, DHHS Publication No. (ADM) 80-1006. Washington, D.C.: U.S. Government Printing Office.

**58.** Karno, M. and Edgerton, R.B.

    1969      Perception of Mental Illness in a Mexican American Community. *Archives of General Psychiatry* 20 (February): 233-238.

**59.** Malzberg, B.

    1956      Mental Disease among Native and Foreign-Born Negroes in New York State. *Journal of Negro Education* 1: 175-181.

**60.** Fitzpatrick, J.P. and Gould, R.

    1968      *Mental Health Needs of Spanish-Speaking Children in the New York Area.* New York: Institute for Social Research, Fordham University.

**61.** National Institute of Mental Health

    1976a      *Services to the Mentally Disabled of Metropolitan Community Mental Health Catchment Area.* Series B, No. 10, DHEW Publication No. (ADM) 76-373. Washington, D.C.: U.S. Government Printing Office.

**62.** National Institute of Mental Health

    1976b      *Services to the Mentally Disabled of Selected Catchment Areas in Eastern New York State and New York City.* DHEW Publication No. (ADM) 76-372. Washington, D.C.: U.S. Government Printing Office.

**63.** Alers, J.O.
1978       *Puerto Ricans and Health: Findings from New York City.*
Bronx, New York: Hispanic Research Center, Fordham University
(Monograph No. 1).

**64.** Canino, I. et al., *op. cit.,* Note 14.

**65.** Abad, V.; Ramos, J.; and Boyce, E.
1974       A Model for Delivery of Mental Health Services to Spanish-
Speaking Minorities. *American Journal of Orthopsychiatry* 44 (4): 584-595.

**66.** Reissman, F. and Scribner, S.
1965       The Underutilization of Mental Health Services by Workers
and Low Income Groups: Causes and Cures. *American Journal of
Psychiatry* 121: 798-801.

**67.** Andersen, R.; Lewis, S.Z.; Ciachello, A.L.; Aday, L.A.; and Chiu, G.
1981       Access to Medical Care among the Hispanic Population of
the Southwestern United States. *Journal of Health and Social Behavior* 22
(March): 78-89.

**68.** Hoppe, S.K. and Heller, P.L.
1975       Alienation, Familism and the Utilization of Health Services
by Mexican Americans. *Journal of Health and Social Behavior* 16: 304-314.

**69.** Rogler, L.H. and Hollingshead, A.B., 1975, *op. cit.,* Note 37.

**70.** Hanrieder, B. and Mittenthal, R.
1975       *Families Headed by Women in New York City: An Analysis
of 1979 Census Facts:* New York: Community Council of Greater New
York.

**71.** U.S. Bureau of the Census
1963       *Census of Population: 1960. Subject Reports. Final Report
PC (2)-ID, Puerto Ricans in the United States.* Washington, D.C.: U.S.
Government Printing Office.

1973       *Census of Population: 1970. Subject Reports. Final Report
PC (2)-IE, Puerto Ricans in the United States.* Washington, D.C.: U.S.
Government Printing Office.

**72.** Keefe, S.E.; Padilla, A.; and Carlos, M.
1978       The Mexican American Extended Family as an Emotional
Support System. In J.M. Casas and S.E. Keefe (eds.), *Family and Mental
Health in the Mexican American Community.* Los Angeles: Spanish

Speaking Mental Health Research Center, University of California (Monograph No. 7).

Keefe, S.E.
1978        Why Mexican Americans Underutilize Mental Health Clinics: Facts and Fallacy. In *Ibid*.

73. Miranda, M.R.
1980        The Family Natural Support System in Hispanic Communities: Preliminary Research Notes and Recommendations. In R.Valle and W.Vega (eds.), *Hispanic Natural Support Systems: Mental Health Promotion Perspectives*. State of California: Department of Mental Health.

74. Padilla, A.; Carlos, M.; and Keefe, S.E.
1976        Mental Health Utilization by Mexican Americans. In M.R. Miranda (ed.), *Psychotherapy with the Spanish Speaking: Issues in Research and Service Delivery*. Los Angeles: Spanish Speaking Mental Health Research Center, University of California (Monograph No. 3), p. 19.

75. Keefe, S.E. et al., *op. cit.,* p. 65, Note 72.

76. Rogler, L.H. and Hollingshead, A.B.; 1975, *op. cit.,* Note 37.

77. Tumin, M.M. and Feldman, A.S.
1961        *Social Class and Social Change in Puerto Rico*. Princeton, New Jersey: Princeton University Press.

78. Wolf, K.L.
1952        Growing Up and its Price in Three Puerto Rican Subcultures. *Psychiatry* 15: 401-433.

79. Landy, D.
1959        *Tropical Childhood: Cultural Transmission and Learning in a Rural Puerto Rican Village*. Chapel Hill, North Carolina: University of North Carolina Press.

80. Roberts, L. and Stefani, L.R.
1949        *Patterns of Living in Puerto Rican Families*. Rio Piedras: Editorial Universitaria.

81. Hill, R.; Stycos, J.; and Back, K.W.
1959        *The Family and Population Control: A Puerto Rican Experiment in Social Change*. Chapel Hill, North Carolina: University of North Carolina Press.

**82.** Rogler, L.H. and Hollingshead, A.B., 1975, *op. cit.,* Note 37.

**83.** Hollingshead, A.B. and Rogler, L.H.
1982        Lower Socio-Economic Status and Mental Illness. *Sociology and Social Research* 46 (4): 387-396.

**84.** Mintz, S.W.
1956        Cañamelar: The Subculture of a Rural Sugar Plantation Proletariat. In J.H. Steward et al. (eds.), *The People of Puerto Rico: A Study in Social Anthropology.* Urbana: University of Illinois Press.

**85.** Brameld, T.
1959        *The Remaking of a Culture: Life and Education in Puerto Rico.* New York: Harper and Brothers, Publishers.

**86.** Rogler, L.H. and Hollingshead, A.B., 1975, *op. cit.,* Note 37.

**87.** Cochran, T.C.
1959        *The Puerto Rican Businessman: A Study in Cultural Change.* Philadelphia: University of Pennsylvania Press.

**88.** Rogler, L.H.
1978        Help Patterns, the Family, and Mental Health: Puerto Ricans in the United States. *International Migration Review* 12 (2): 248-259.

**89.** Fitzpatrick, J.P.
1971        *Puerto Rican Americans: The Meaning of Migration to the Mainland.* Englewood Cliffs, New Jersey: Prentice-Hall.

**90.** Rogler, L.H.; Cooney, R.S.; and Ortiz, V.
1979        Intergenerational Change in Ethnic Identity in the Puerto Rican Family. *International Migration Review* 14, 2: 193-214.

**91.** Rogler, C.C.
1940        *Comerio: A Study of a Puerto Rican Town.* Kansas: Department of Journalism Press, p. 61.

**92.** Wolf, E.R.
1956        San Jose: Subcultures of a 'Traditional' Coffee Municipality. In J.H. Steward et al., (eds.), *op. cit.,* Note 84.

**93.** Steward, J.H., et al., (eds.)
1956        *The People of Puerto Rico: A Study in Social Anthropology.* Urbana: University of Illinois Press, p. 474.

Rogler, L.H.
1967    Slum Neighborhoods in Latin America. *Journal of Inter-American Studies* 9 (4): 507-528.

94. Caplow, T.; Stryker, S.; and Wallace, S.E.
1964    *The Urban Ambience*. Totowa, New Jersey: The Bedminster Press.

95. Fitzpatrick, J.P., *op. cit.*, Note 89, pp. 81-82.

96. Rogler, L.H. and Hollingshead, A.B., 1975, *op. cit.*, Note 37.

97. Keefe, S.E.; Padilla, A.M.; and Carlos, M.L., *op. cit.*, Note 72.

98. Rogler, L.H. and Hollingshead, A.B., 1975, *op. cit.*, Note 37.

99. Rogler, L.H. and Hollingshead, A.B.
1960    Algunas observaciones sobre el espiritismo y las enfermedades mentales entre puertorriqueños de clase baja. *Revista de Ciencias Sociales,* 4 (1): 141-150.

1961    The Puerto Rican Spiritualist as a Psychiatrist. *American Journal of Sociology* 67 (1): 17-21.

1975    *Op. Cit.*, Note 37.

100. Wakefield, D., *op. cit.*, Note 50.

Garrison, V., *op. cit.*, Note 50.

Harwood, A., *op. cit.*, Note 50.

101. Arenas, S.; Cross, H.; and Willard, W.
1980    *Curanderos* and Mental Health Professionals: A Comparative Study on Perceptions of Psychopathology. *Hispanic Journal of Behavorial Sciences* 2 (4): 407-421.

102. Abad, V.; Ramos, J.; and Boyce, E.; *op. cit.*, Note 65.

103. Bluestone, H. and Purdy, B.
1977    Psychiatric Services to Puerto Rican Patients in the Bronx. In E.R. Padilla and A.M. Padilla (eds.), *Transcultural Psychiatry: An Hispanic Perspective*. Los Angeles: Spanish Speaking Mental Health Research Center, University of California (Monograph No. 4).

**104.** Herrera, A.E. and Sanchez, V.C.

1976    Behaviorally Oriented Group Therapy: A Successful Application in the Treatment of Low Income Spanish-Speaking Clients. In M.R. Miranda (ed.), *op. cit.,* Note 74.


Keefe, S.E.

1978    Why Mexican Americans Underutilize Mental Health Clinics: Facts and Fallacy. In J.M. Casas and S.E. Keefe (eds.), *op. cit.,* Note 72.

**105.** Castro, F.G.

1977    Level of Acculturation and Related Considerations in Psychotherapy with Spanish-Speaking/Surnamed Clients. Los Angeles: Spanish Speaking Mental Health Research Center, University of California (Occasional Paper No. 3).

**106.** Padilla, A.M.; Ruiz, R.A.; and Alvarez, R., *op. cit.,* Note 20.

**107.** Keefe, S.E. and Casas, J.M.

1978    Family and Mental Health Among Mexican Americans: Some Considerations for Mental Health Services. In J.M. Casas and S.E. Keefe (eds.), *op. cit.,* Note 72.

**108.** Karno, M. and Edgerton, R.B., *op. cit.,* Note 58.

**109.** Vega, W.

1980    The Hispanic Natural Healer, a Case Study: Implications for Prevention. In R. Valle and W. Vega (eds.), op. cit., Note 73.

**110.** Keefe, S.E. and Casas, J.M., *op. cit.,* Note 107.

**111.** Rogler, L.H. and Hollingshead, A.B., 1975, *op. cit.,* Note 37.

**112.** Ralph J.R.

1977    Voodoo, Spiritualism and Psychiatry: A Summary of a Panel Discussion. In E.R. Padilla and A.M. Padilla (eds.), *op. cit.,* Note 103.

**113.** Padilla, A.M.; Carlos, M.L.; and Keefe, S.E., *op. cit.,* Note 74.

**114.** Bloom, B.

1975    *Changing Patterns of Psychiatric Care.* New York: Human Sciences Press.

**115.** Trevino, F.M.; Bruhn, J.G.; and Bunce, H., III
    1979        Utilization of Community Mental Health Services in a Texas-Mexico Border City. *Social Science and Medicine* 13 (3A): 331-334.

**116.** *Ibid.,* p. 334.

**117.** Edgerton, R.B. and Karno, M.
    1971        Mexican-American Bilingualism and the Perception of Mental Illness. *Archives of General Psychiatry* 24: 286-290.

*118. Ibid.*

**119.** Keefe, S.E., *op. cit.,* Note 104.

**120.** Velez, C.G.
    1980        *Mexicano/Hispano* Support Systems and *Confianza:* Theoretical Issues of Cultural Adaptation. In R. Valle and W. Vega (eds.), *op. cit.,* Note 73.

    Romero, J.T.
    1980        Hispanic Support Systems: Health-Mental Health Promotion Strategies. In R. Valle and W. Vega (eds.), *op. cit.,* Note 73.

**121.** Abad, V.; Ramos, J.; and Boyce, E., *op. cit.,* Note 65.

**122.** Bluestone, H. and Purdy, B., *op. cit.,* Note 103.

    Abad, V.; Ramos, J.; and Bouce, E., *op. cit.,* Note 65.

**123.** Karno, M., and Edgerton, R.B., *op. cit.,* Note 58.

    Edgerton, R.B. and Karno, M., *op. cit.,* Note 117.

**124.** Newton, F.
    1978        The Mexican American Emic System of Mental Illness: An Exploratory Study: In J.M. Casas and S.E. Keefe (eds.), *op. cit.,* Note 72.

    Padilla, A.; Ruiz, R.; and Alverez, R., *op. cit.,* Note 20.

    Arenas, S.; Cross, H.; and Willard, W., *op. cit.,* Note 101.

**125.** Edgerton, R.B. and Karno, M., *op. cit.,* Note 117.

**126.** Rogler, L.H. and Hollingshead, A.B., 1975, *op. cit.,* Note 37.

127. Riessman, F. and Scribner, S., *op. cit.,* Note 66.

128. Fabrega, H., Jr.; Swartz, J.D.; and Wallace, C.A.
1968      Ethnic Differences in Psychopathology II — Specific Differences with Emphasis on a Mexican American Group. *Psychiatric Research* 6 (3): 221-235.

129. Newton, F., *op. cit.,* Note 123.

130. Rogler, L.H. and Hollingshead, A.B., 1975, *op. cit.,* Note 37.

131. Hollingshead, A.B. and Redlich, F.C., *op. Cit.,* Note 5.

132. Lorion, R.P.
1973      Socioeconomic Status and Traditional Treatment Approaches Reconsidered. *Psychological Bulletin* 79 (4): 263-270.

1974      Patient and Therapist Variables in the Treatment of Low-Income Patients. *Psychological Bulletin* 81 (6): 344-354.

133. *Ibid.,* 1974.

134. Padilla, A.; Ruiz, R.; and Alvarez, R.; *op. cit.,* Note 20.

135. Riessman, F. and Scribner, S., *op. cit.,* Note 66.

136. Padilla, A.; Ruiz, R.; and Alvarez, R., *op. cit.,* Note 20.

137. Karno, M. and Edgerton, R.B., *op. cit.,* Note 58.

Padilla, A.; Ruiz, R.; and Alvarez, R., *op. cit.,* Note 20.

Keefe, S.E., *op. cit.,* Note 104.

138. Padilla, A.; Carlos, M.; and Keefe, S.E., *op. cit.,* Note 74.

139. Karno, M.
1966      The Enigma of Ethnicity in a Psychiatric Clinic. *Archives of General Psychiatry* 14: 516-520.

140. Vega, W.
1980      Mental Health Research and North American Hispanic Populations: A Review and a Proposed Research Strategy. In R. Valle and W. Vega (eds.), *op. cit.,* Note 73.

**141.** Rogler, L.H. and Hollingshead, A.B., 1975, *op. cit.,* Note 37.

**142.** Fernandez-Marina, R.
1961    The Puerto Rican Syndrome: Its Diagnosis and Cultural Determinants. *Psychiatry* 24: 79-82.

Mehlman, R.
1961    The Puerto Rican Syndrome. *American Journal of Psychiatry* 11 (8): 328-332.

**143.** Rogler, L.H. and Hollingshead, A.B., 1975, *op. cit.,* Note 37, p. 248.

**144.** *Ibid.,* p. 249.

**145.** National Institute of Mental Health
1976c    *A Working Manual of Simple Program Evaluation Techniques for Community Mental Health Centers.* DHEW Publication No. (ADM) 79-404. Washington, D.C.: U.S. Government Printing Office.

**146.** Freidson, E.
1961    *Patients' Views of Medical Practice. A Study of Subscribers to a Prepaid Medical Plan in the Bronx.* New York: Russell Sage Foundation.

1970    *Profession of Medicine. A Study of the Sociology of Applied Knowledge.* New York: Dodd, Mead and Company.

**147.** Suchman, E.A.
1964    Sociomedical Variations among Ethnic Groups. *American Journal of Sociology* 70: 319-331.

**148.** Bloom, B., *op. cit.,* Note 114.

Trevino, F.M.; Bruhn, J.G.; and Bunce, H., III, *op. cit.,* Note 115.

**149.** Rodriguez, O.
1983    A Profile of Services Utilization in the Fordham-Tremont Area: Preliminary Report. *Hispanic Research Center Research Bulletin* 6 (1-2).

**150.** Dohrenwend, B.P.; Shout, P.E.; Egri, G.; and Mendelsohn, F.S.
1980    Non-Specific Measures of Psychological Distress and Other Dimensions of Psychopathology. *Archives of General Psychiatry* 37: 1229-1236.

**151.** Durrett, M.E. and Kim, C.C.

1973    A Comparative Study of Behavioral Maturity in Mexican American and Anglo Preschool Children. *Journal of Genetic Psychology* 123: 55-62.

**152.** Haberman, P.W.
1976    Psychiatric Symptoms Among Puerto Ricans in Puerto Rico and New York City. *Ethnicity* 3 (2): 133-144.

**153.** Kagan, S. and Romero, C.
1977    Non-Adaptive Assertiveness of Anglo American and Mexican American Children of Two Ages. *Interamerican Journal of Psychology* 11: 27-32. (Abstract).

**154.** LeVine, E.S. and Padilla, A.M.
1980    *Crossing Cultures in Therapy: Pluralistic Counseling for the Hispanic.* Monterey, California: Brooks/Cole Publishing.

**155.** Korchin, S.J.
1976    *Modern Clinical Psychology: Principles of Intervention in the Clinic and Community.* New York: Basic Books.

**156.** Reschly, D.J.
1981    Psychological Testing in Educational Classification and Placement. *American Psychologist* 36 (10): 1094-1102.

Mercer, J.
1976    Pluralistic Diagnosis in the Evaluation of Black and Chicano Children: A Procedure for Taking Sociocultural Variables into Account in Clinical Assessment. In C.A. Hernandez, M.J. Haug, and N.N. Wagner (eds.), *Chicanos: Social and Psychological Perspectives* (2nd edition). St. Louis, Missouri: C.V. Mosby Co.

Garcia, J.
1977    Intelligence Testing: Quotients, Quotas, and Quackery. In J.L. Martinez, Jr. (ed.), *Chicano Psychology.* New York: Academic Press.

McClelland, D.C.
1973    Testing for Competence Rather than for 'Intelligence'. *American Psychologist* 28 (1): 1-14.

**157.** Cole, N.S.
1981    Bias in Testing. *American Psychologist* 36 (10): 1067-1077.

**158.** Marcos, L.R.
1980    The Psychiatric Evaluation and Psychotherapy of the

Hispanic Bilingual Patient. *Hispanic Research Center Research Bulletin* 3 (2): 1-7.

159. Sabin, J.E.
     1975        Translating Despair. *American Journal of Psychiatry* 132 (2): 197-199.

160. Marcos, L.R.; Alpert, M.; Urcuyo, L.; and Kesselman, M.
     1973        The Effect of Interview Language on the Evaluation of Psychopathology in Spanish-American Schizophrenia Patients. *American Journal of Psychiatry* 130 (5); 549-553.

161. Mercer, J.R.
     1977        Identifying the Gifted Chicano Child. In J.L. Martinez, Jr. (ed.), *Chicano Psychology*. New York: Academic Press.

162. *Ibid.*

163. Ortiz, A.C. and Ball, C.
     1977        The Enchilada Test. In R. Oakland (ed.), *Psychological and Educational Assessment of Minority Children*. New York: Brunner/Mazel.

164. Mercer, J.R., *op. cit.,* Note 161.

165. LeVine, E.S. and Padilla, A.M., *op. cit.,* Note 154.

166. Rogler, L.H. and Hollingshead, A.B., *op. cit.,* Note 37.

167. Grace, W.J.
     1959        Ataque. *New York Medicine* 15 (1): 12-13. (Abstract).

168. LeVine, E.S. and Padilla, A.M., *op. cit.,* Note 154.

169. Lopez, S.
     1977        Clinical Stereotypes of Mexican Americans. In J.L. Martinez, Jr. (ed.), *op. cit.,* Note 161.

170. Baskin, D.; Bluestone, H.; and Nelson, M.
     1981a       Ethnicity and Psychiatric Diagnosis. *Journal of Clinical Psychology* 37 (3): 529-537.

171. Baskin, D.; Bluestone, H.; and Nelson, M.
     1981b       Mental Illness in Minority Women. *Journal of Clinical Psychology* 37 (3): 491-498.

**172.** Velikovsky, I.

1934    Can a Newly Acquired Language Become the Speech of the Unconscious? *Psychoanalytic Quarterly* 3: 329-335.

**173.** Buxbaum, E.

1949    The Role of the Second Language in the Formation of the Ego and Superego. *Psychoanalytic Quarterly* 18: 279-289.

**174.** Greenson, R.

1950    The Mother Tongue and the Mother. *International Journal of Psychoanalysis* 31: 18-23.

Krapf, E.

1955    The Choice of Language in Polyglot Psychoanalysis. *Psychoanalytic Quarterly* 24: 343-357.

Peck, E.

1974    The Relationship of Disease and Other Stress to Second Language. *International Journal of Social Psychiatry* 20 (1-2): 128-133.

Marcos, L.R.

1976    Bilinguals in Psychotherapy: Language as an Emotional Barrier. *American Journal of Psychotherapy* 30 (4): 552-560.

Marcos, L.R. and Alpert, M.

1976    Strategies and Risks in Psychotherapy with Bilingual Patients: The Phenomenon of Language Independence. *American Journal of Psychiatry* 133 (11): 1275-1278.

**175.** Laski, E. and Taleporos, E.

1977    Anticholinergic Psychosis in a Bilingual Case Study. *American Journal of Psychiatry* 134 (9): 1038-1040.

**176.** Lipsius, L.

1975    Electroconvulsive Therapy and Language. *American Journal of Psychiatry* 132 (4): 459 (Letter to the Editor).

**177.** Revitch, E.

1975    Aphasia in Polyglots. *American Journal of Psychiatry* 132 (11): 1221 (Letter to the Editor).

**178.** Fitzpatrick, J.P. and Gould, R., *op. cit.,* Note 60.

**179.** Gross, H.; Knatterud, G.; and Donner, L.

1969    The Effect of Race and Sex on the Variation of Diagnosis and Disposition in the Psychiatric Emergency Room. *Journal of Nervous and Mental Diseases* 148: 638-642.

180. Baskin, D.; Bluestone, H.; and Nelson, M., 1981a, *op. cit.,* Note 170.

181. Fitzpatrick, J.P. and Gould, R., *op. cit.,* Note 60.

182. Gross, H.; Knatterud, G.; and Donner, L., *op. cit.,* Note 179.

183. Karno, M.
1966        The Enigma of Ethnicity in a Psychiatric Clinic. *Archives of General Psychiatry* 14: 516-520.

184. Thomas, A.
1962        Pseudotransference Reactions Due to Cultural Stereotyping. *American Journal of Orthopsychiatry* 32: 894-900.

185. Carkhuff, R. and Pierce, R.
1967        Differential Effects of Therapist Race and Social Class upon Depth of Self-Exploration in the Initial Clinical Interview. *Journal of Consulting Psychology* 31: 632-634.

186. Karno, M. and Edgerton, R.B., *op. cit.,* Note 58.

187. Edgerton, R.B. and Karno, M., *op. cit.,* Note 117.

188. Peck, E., *op. cit.,* Note 174.

189. Del Castillo, J.
1970        The Influence of Language upon Symptomatology in Foreign-Born Patients. *American Journal of Psychiatry* 127: 242-244.

190. Marcos, L.R.; Alpert, M.; Urcuyo, L.; and Kesselman, M., *op. cit.,* Note 160.

Marcos, L.R.; Urcuyo, L.; Kesselman, M.; and Alpert, M.
1973        The Language Barrier in Evaluating Spanish-American Patients. *Archives of General Psychiatry* 29: 655-659.

191. Price, C. and Cuellar, I.
1981        Effects of Language and Related Variables on the Expression of Psychopathology in Mexican Americans. *Hispanic Journal of Behavioral Sciences* 3 (2): 145-160.

192. Vazquez, C.A.

1982       Research on the Psychiatric Evaluation of the Bilingual Patient: A Methodological Critique. *Hispanic Journal of Behavioral Sciences* 4 (1): 75-80.

**193.** Thompson, C.E.
1949       The Thompson Modification of the Thematic Apperception Test. *Journal of Projective Techniques* 13: 469-478.

Williams, R.
1977       The BITCH-100: A Culture Specific Test. In R. Oakland (ed.), *op. cit.,* Note 163.

**194.** Ortiz, A.C. and Ball, C., *op. cit.,* Note 163.

Struthers, J. and De Avila, E.A.
1977       Development of a Group Measure to Assess the Extent of Prelogical and Precausal Thinking in Primary School-Age Children. In R. Oakland (ed.), *op. cit.,* Note 163.

**195.** Oakland, R. (ed.)
1977       *Psychological and Educational Assessment of Minority Children.* New York: Brunner/Mazel.

**196.** Auld, F., Jr.
1952       Influence of Social Class on Personality Test Responses. *Psychological Bulletin* 49: 318-332.

Ames, L.M. and August, J.
1966       Rorschach Responses of Negro and White 5- to 10-Year Olds. *Journal of Genetic Psychology* 109: 297-309.

Riessman, F. and Scribner, S., *op. cit.,* Note 66.

Booth, L.J.
1960       A Normative· Comparison of the Responses of Latin American and Anglo American Children to the Children's Apperception Test. In M.R. Haworth (ed.), *The C.A.T.: Facts about Fantasy.* New York: Grune and Stratton.

**197.** Cole, M. and Bruner, J.S.
1971       Cultural Differences and Inferences about Psychological Processes. *American Psychologist* 26 (10): 867-876.

Thompson, C.E., *op. cit.,* Note 193.

Laosa, L.N.
1973        Reform in Educational and Psychological Assessment: Cultural and Linguistic Issues. *Journal of the Association of Mexican American Educators* 1: 10-24.

McClelland, D.C., *op. cit.,* Note 156.

Riessman, F. and Scribner, S., *op. cit.,* Note 66.

Thompson, C.E., *op. cit.,* Note 193.

**199.** Murray, H.A.
1943        *The Thematic Apperception Test.* Cambridge, Massachusetts: Harvard University Press.

**200.** Bailey, B.E. and Green, J., III
1977        Black Thematic Apperception Test Stimulus Material. *Journal of Personality Assessment* 41 (1): 25-30.

**201.** Korchin, S.; Mitchell, H.; and Meltzoff, J.A.
1950        A Critical Evaluation of the Thompson Thematic Apperception Test. *Journal of Projective Techniques* 13: 445-452.

Schwartz, E.; Reiss, B.; and Cottingham, A.
1951        Further Critical Evaluation of the Negro Version of the TAT. *Journal of Projective Techniques* 15: 394-400.

Cook, R.A.
1953        Identification and Ego Defensiveness in Thematic Apperception. *Journal of Projective Techniques* 17: 312-315.

Light, B.H.
1955        A Further Test of the Thompson TAT Rationale. *Journal of Abnormal Social Psychology* 51: 148-150.

**202.** Murstein, B.I.
1963        *Theory and Research in Projective Techniques (Emphasizing the TAT).* New York: John Wiley and Sons.

**203.** Bailey, B.E. and Green, J., III, *op. cit.,* Note 200.

**204.** Cowan, G. and Goldberg, E.
1967        Need Achievement as a Function of the Race and Sex of Figures in Selected TAT Cards. *Journal of Personality and Social Psychology* 5: 245-249.

205. Bailey, B.E. and Green, J., III, *op. cit.,* Note 200.

206. Costantino, G.
1978       *Preliminary Report on TEMAS: A New Thematic Apperception Test to Assess Ego Functions in Ethnic Minority Children.* Paper presented at the Second American Conference on Fantasy and the Imaging Process, Chicago (November).

207. Costantino, G.; Malgady, R.G.; and Vazquez, C.
1981       A Comparison of the Murray-TAT and a New Thematic Apperception Test for Urban Hispanic Children. *Hispanic Journal of Behavioral Sciences* 3 (3): 291-300.

208. U.S. Bureau of the Census
1973       Persons of Spanish Origin. *Census of Population: 1970.* Subject Reports. Final Report PC(2)-1C. Washington, D.C.: U.S. Government Printing Office.

1979       Persons of Spanish Origin in the United States: March 1979 (Advance Report). *Current Population Reports,* Series P-20, No. 347. Washington, D.C.: U.S. Government Printing Office.

209. Hollingshead, A.B. and Redlich, F.C., *op. cit.,* Note 5.

210. Myers, J.K. and Bean, L.L.
1968       *A Decade Later: A Follow-Up of Social Class and Mental Illness.* New York: John Wiley and Sons.

211. Lorion, R.P.
1978       Research on Psychotherapy and Behavior Change with the Disadvantaged. In S.L. Garfield, A.E. Bergin (eds.), *Handbook of Psychotherapy and Behavior Change: An Empirical Analysis* (2nd ed.). New York: John Wiley and Sons.

Parloff, M.B.; Waskow, I.E.; and Wolfe, B.E.
1978       Research and Therapist Variables in Relation to Process and Outcome. In *Ibid.*

Sue, D.W. (ed.)
1981       *Counseling the Culturally Different: Theory and Practice.* New York: John Wiley and Sons.

212. Schofield, W.
1964       *Psychotherapy: The Purchase of Friendship.* Englewood Cliffs, New Jersey: Prentice-Hall.

213. Goldstein, A.P. and Simonson, N.
    1971        Social Psychological Approaches to Psychotherapy
Research. In S.L. Garfield and A.E. Bergin (eds.), Handbook of Psycho-
therapy and Behavior Change: An Empirical Analysis (1st ed.). New York:
John Wiley and Sons.

214. Adams, P.L. and McDonald, N.F.
    1968        Clinical "Cooling Out" of Poor People. *American Journal
of Orthopsychiatry* 38: 457-463.

215. Garfield, S.L.
    1981        Psychotherapy: A Forty Year Appraisal. *American
Psychologist* 36 (2): 174-183.

216. Teichner, V.J.; Cadden, J.J.; and Berry, G.W.
    1981        The Puerto Rican Patient: Some Historical, Cultural and
Psychological Aspects. *Journal of the American Academy of Psychoanalysis* 9 (2): 277-289.

217. Green, J.M.; Trankina, F.J.; and Chavez, N.
    1976        Therapeutic Intervention with Mexican American Children.
*Psychiatric Annals* 6 (5): 59-75.

218. Szapocznik, J.; Santisteban, D.; Hervis, O.; Spencer, F.; and Kurtines,
    W.M.

    1981        Treatment of Depression among Cuban American Elders:
Some Validational Evidence for a Life Enhancement Counseling Approach.
*Journal of Consulting and Clinical Psychology* 49 (5): 752-754.

    Johnson, D.L.; Leler, H.; Rios, L.B.L.; Kahn, A.J.; Mazeika, E.;
    Frede, M.; and Bisett, B.
    1974        The Houston Parent-Child Development Center: A Parent
Education Program for Mexican American Families. *American Journal of
Orthopsychiatry* 44: 121-128.

    Boulette, T.R.
    1977        Parenting: Special Needs of Low-Income Spanish-Surnamed
Families. *Psychiatric Annals* 6: 95-107.

219. Fink, A.K.
    1967        Psychodrama in the Puerto Rican Setting. *Group Psycho-
therapy* 20: 121-122.

220. Maes, W.R. and Rinaldi, J.R.

1974        Counseling the Chicano Child. *Elementary School Guidance and Counseling* 8: 279-284.

**221.** Herrara, A.E. and Sanchez, V.C.
1976        Behaviorally Oriented Group Therapy: A Successful Application in the Treatment of Low-Income Spanish-Speaking Clients. In M. Miranda (ed.), *op. cit.,* Note 74.

Boulette, T.R.
1976        Assertive Training with Low-Income Mexican American Women. In M. Miranda (ed.), *Ibid.*

**222.** Szapocznik, J.; Santisteban, D.; Kurtines, W.N.; Hervis, O.; and Spencer, F.
1981        Life Enhancement Counseling: Treating Depression among Hispanic Elders. Paper presented at the Society of Psychotherapy Research Meeting, Aspen, Colorado (June).

**223.** Maldonado-Sierra, E.D. and Trent, R.D.
1960        The Sibling Relationship in Group Psychotherapy with Puerto Rican Schizophrenics. *American Journal of Psychiatry* 117 (3): 239-244.

**224.** Ruiz, R.A.
1981        Cultural and Historical Perspectives in Counseling Hispanics. In D.W. Sue (ed.), *op. cit.,* Note 211.

**225.** Sue, D.W. (ed.), *op. cit.,* Note 211.

**226.** Miranda, M.R. (ed.)
1976        *Psychotherapy with the Spanish-Speaking: Issues in Research and Service Delivery.* Los Angeles: Spanish Speaking Mental Health Research Center, University of California (Monograph No. 3).

**227.** Baekeland, F. and Lundwell, L.
1975        Dropping Out of Treatment: A Critical Review. *Psychological Bulletin* 82 (5): 738-783.

**228.** Maslow, A.H.
1962        *Toward a Psychology of Being.* Princeton, New Jersey: Van Nostrand Press.

**229.** Acosta, F.X.
1980        Self-Described Reasons for Premature Termination of Psychotherapy by Mexican American, Black American, and Anglo American

Patients. *Psychological Reports* 47 (2): 435-443.

**230.** Acosta, F.X.; Evans, L.A.; Yamamoto, J.; and Wilcox, S.A.
1980        Helping Minority and Low-Income Psychotherapy Patients
"Tell it Like it Is." *The Journal of Biocommunication* 7 (3): 13-19.

**231.** National Coalition of Hispanic Mental Health and Human Services
Organizations (COSSMHO)
1981        Cross-Cultural Orientation Program at U.S.C. Trains
Therapists, Low-Income Patients to Work Together. *The Reporter* 7 (4): 1, 7.

**232.** Acosta, F.X. et al., *op. cit.,* Note 230.

Heitler, J.B.
1976        Preparatory Techniques in Initiating Expressive Psychotherapy with Lower Class, Unsophisticated Patients. *Psychological Bulletin*
83 (2): 339-352.

Fields, S.
1979        Telling it Like it Is. *Innovations* (Summer): 3-7.

**233.** Parloff, M.B. et al., *op. cit.,* Note 211.

**234.** Sue, D.W. (ed.), *op. cit.,* Note 211.

**235.** Acosta, F.X. and Scheehan, J.G.
1977        Preferences Toward Mexican American and Anglo
American Psychotherapists. *Journal of Consulting·and Clinical Psychology*
44 (2): 272-279.

**236.** Cross, W.C. and Maldonado, B.
1971        The Counselor, the Mexican American, and the Stereotype.
*Elementary School Guidance and Counseling* 6: 25-31.

**237.** Korchin, S.J.
1976        *Modern Clincial Psychology: Principles of Intervention in
the Clinic and Community.* New York: Basic Books.

**238.** Sue, D.W. (ed.), *op. cit.,* Note 211, p. 37.

**239.** Rogers, C.R.
1957        The Necessary and Sufficient Conditions of Therapeutic
Personality Change. *Journal of Consulting Psychology* 21: 93-103.

**240.** *Ibid.*

**241.** Green, J.M. et al., *op. cit.,* Note 217.

**242.** Garfield, S.L., *op. cit.,* Note 215.

**243.** Eysenck, H.
1952      The Effects of Psychotherapy: An Evaluation. *Journal of Consulting Psychology* 16: 319-324.

**244.** Luborsky, L.; Singer, B.; and Luborsky, L.
1975      Comparative Studies of Psychotherapies. *Archives of General Psychiatry* 32: 995-1008.

**245.** Smith, M.L. and Glass, G.V.
1977      Meta-Analysis of Psychotherapy Outcome Studies. *American Psychologist* 32 (9): 752-760.

**246.** Lorion, R.P., 1978, *op. cit.,* Note 211.

**247.** Garfield, S.L., *op. cit.,* Note 215.

**248.** Paul, G.L.
1967      Strategy of Outcome Research in Psychotherapy. *Journal of Consulting Psychology* 31 (2): 109-118.

**249.** Boulette, T.R.
1975      *Determining Needs and Appropriate Counseling Approaches for Mexican American Women: A Comparison of Therapeutic Listening and Behavioral Research.* San Francisco: R and E Associates.

**250.** Acosta, F.X. and Scheehan, J.G., *op. cit.,* Note 235.

**251.** Frank, J.D.
1961      *Persuasion and Healing.* Baltimore: Johns Hopkins University Press.

1974      Therapeutic Components of Psychotherapy. *Journal of Nervous and Mental Diseases* 159 (3): 25-42.

**252.** Heffernon, A. and Bruehl, D.
1971      Some Effects of Race of Inexperienced Lay Counselors on Black Junior High School Students. *Journal of School Psychology* 9: 35-37.

**253.** Munoz, J.A.
1981      Difficulties of a Hispanic American Psychotherapist in the Treatment of Hispanic American Patients. *American Journal of Ortho-*

*psychiatry* 5 (4): 646-653.

**254.** Cummings, N.A.
1977        Anatomy and Psychotherapy under National Health Insurance. *American Psychologist* 32 (9): 711-718.

**255.** Barrett, C.L.; Hampe, I.E.; and Miller, L.
1978        Research on Psychotherapy with Children. In S.L. Garfield and A.E. Bergin (eds.), *Handbook of Psychotherapy and Behavior Change: An Empirical Analysis* (2nd ed.). New York: John Wiley and Sons.

**256.** Padilla, A.M.; Ruiz, R.A.; and Alvarez, R., *op. cit.*, Note 20.

**257.** Special Sub-Task Panel on Mental Health of Hispanic Americans, *op. cit.*, Note 2.

**258.** *Ibid.*

**259.** Kramer, M.
1976        *Report to the President's Biomedical Research Panel.* Washington, D.C.: U.S. Government Printing Office.

**260.** Special Populations Sub-Task Panel, *op. cit.*, Note 2.

**261.** Canino, I.A.; Earley, B.F.; and Rogler, L.H., *op. cit.*, Note 14.

**262.** Seville-Troike, M.
1973        *Bilingual Children: A Resource Document.* Arlington, Virginia: The Center for Applied Linguistics.

**263.** Auld, F., Jr., *op. cit.*, Note 196.

**264.** McCormick, C.H.; and Karabinus, R.A.
1976        Relationship of Ethnic Groups' Self-Esteem and Anxiety to School Success. *Educational and Psychological Measurement* 36 (4): 1093-1100.

**265.** Bettelheim, B.
1977        *The Uses of Enchantment: The Importance and Meaning of Fairy Tales.* New York: Vintage Books.

**266.** Gardner, R.
1971        *Therapeutic Communication with Childen: The Mutual Story-Telling Technique.* New York: Science House.

**267.** Saltz, E. and Johnson, J.
1973    *Training for Thematic Fantasy Play in Culturally Disadvantaged Children: Preliminary Results.* Center for the Study of Cognitive Processes, Wayne State University.

**268.** Amato, A.; Emans, R.; and Ziegler, E.
1973    The Effectiveness of Creative Dramatics and Storytelling in a Library Setting. *The Journal of Educational Research* 67: 161-162.

**269.** Bettelheim, B., *op. cit., Note 265.*

**270.** Costantino, G.
1982    *Cuentos Folkloricos:* A New Therapy Modality with Puerto Rican Children. *Hispanic Research Center Research Bulletin* 5 (4): 7-10.

**271.** Special Populations Sub-Task Panel, *op. cit.,* Note 2.

**272.** Bessuk, E.L. and Gerson, S.
1978    Deinstitutionalization and Mental Health Services. *Scientific American* 238 (2): 46-53.

**273.** Goldstein, A.P.
1981    *Psychological Skill Training: The Structured Technique.* New York: Pergamon Press.

**274.** Myers, J.K. and Bean, L.L., *op. cit.,* Note 210.

**275.** Zigler, E. and Phillips, L.
1960    Social Effectiveness and Symptomatic Behavior. *Journal of Abnormal and Social Psychology* 161 (2): 231-238.

**276.** Myers, J.K. and Bean, L.L., *op. cit.,* Note 210.

**277.** Amin, A.E.
1974    Culture and Post-Hospital Community Adjustment of Long-Term Hospitalized Puerto Rican Schizophrenic Patients in New York City. (Doctoral dissertation, Columbia University; also *Dissertation Abstracts International* 35, 5964B, University Microfilms #74-26579).

**278.** Garrison, V.
1978    Support Systems of Schizophrenic and Nonschizophrenic Puerto Rican Migrant Women in New York City. *Schizophrenia Bulletin* 4 (1): 561-596.

**279.** Leff, J.P.

1976        Schizophrenia and Sensitivity to the Family Environment. *Schizophrenia Bulletin* 2 (4): 566-574.

280. Rogler, L.H. and Hollingshead, A.B., *op. cit.,* Note 37.

281. Summers, F.
1981        The Post-Acute Functioning of the Schizophrenic. *Journal of Clinical Psychology* 37 (4): 705-714.

282. Wansbrough, N. and Cooper, P.
1980        *Open Employment after Mental Illness.* London: Tavistock Publications.

283. Anthony, W.A.
1980        *The Principles of Psychiatric Rehabilitation.* Baltimore: University Park Press.

284. *Ibid.*

285. Goldstein, A.P., *op. cit.,* Note 273.

286. Wallace, C.J.; Nelson, C.J.; Liberman, R.P.; Archison, R.A.; Lukoff, D.; Elder, J.P.; and Ferris, C.
1980        A Review and Critique of Social Skills Training with Schizophrenic Patients. *Schizophrenia Bulletin* 6 (1): 42-63.